# THE GUILT-FREE GUIDE TO MOTHERHOOD

## Trusting yourself as a mother, through pregnancy and the baby years.

By Kirsten Toyne

THE GUILT-FREE GUIDE TO MOTHERHOOD
Trusting yourself as a mother, through pregnancy and the baby years.

# Acknowledgements

First and foremost, I would like to thank the women who shared their experiences of motherhood so openly with me. Without them this book would not have been possible. Their insights into motherhood really inspired me to continue with this project and make it a reality.

In addition, a hearty thanks to Sharon Fernandez who helped get me started back when The Guilt-Free Guide to Motherhood was only an idea. Along with these women, I also want to thank my two lovely sons who have been my companions throughout my journey as a mother. Through them I have learnt so much about myself.

I also want to thank Teisha Leigh for her guidance, time and friendship throughout the book writing process as well as Sandra Westland and Tom Barber for their support. And last, but by no means least, I want to thank my husband and parents for their love and unwavering belief in me.

# Contents

# Introduction

To be the best mothers we can, we need to accept our own feelings and stop attempting to meet the often impossible demands of modern motherhood. To this end, with the help of twenty-four women with young children and my experience as a counsellor, The Guilt-Free Guide to Motherhood explores the key emotional and practical issues that we face as new mothers, many of which are never talked about.

There are so many pressures for mothers to navigate today. Right from pregnancy through to having our babies, we are met with a barrage of information on what to do and even how to feel. It can seem like there is an endless set of requirements to meet in order to be a good mother. If we were to attempt to adhere to all the things that we 'should' do with our babies, we would go mad or collapse trying. The problem with much of the advice on which technique is best for our children is that one crucial thing gets left out: us. As mothers we are a huge part of the equation. Who we are and how we feel plays a very significant role in our children's lives.

By listening to other women speaking of their experiences it becomes apparent that there is not one way to feel or a right way to be. The Guilt-Free Guide to Motherhood helps you explore your own feelings, expectations and needs, so that you can forge a life that works for you and your baby. This is not a prescriptive guide telling you what you should feel or do; rather it is an exploration of motherhood so that you can understand the process, considering how it relates to you. When we truly comprehend that there is no perfect mother, we are freed up to discover our own way to be a mum, whole and guilt-free.

## How did The Guilt-Free Guide come about?

The first time I was pregnant, I thought the hard thing about being a mother would be knowing how to manage a baby. However, I soon realised that the toughest part was learning how to cope with the emotional demands and the complex feelings that motherhood evokes. After reading lots of books (many giving contradictory advice) I felt there was a massive hole in the information out there, with so many key aspects of motherhood never even being broached. Consequently, I decided to research what motherhood was really like for other women. What I discovered was amazing. The women I interviewed spoke with such honesty about how it was for them, sharing many unspoken aspects of motherhood. I found mothers who loved their children beyond anything words could describe, all doing the best they could. One of the noticeable aspects was the pressure they were under, frequently leaving them feeling that they were not doing well enough. This is what made me choose the title: The Guilt-Free Guide to Motherhood.

## Who are the women interviewed?

This book is based on questionnaires and in-depth interviews with twenty-four women, as well as my experience as an Integrative Counsellor. All of my women (whose ages ranged from twenty-three to forty-one) were still in the throes of intensive mothering, with little ones from four months to twenty-three months old. They came from a range of social backgrounds, from those in temporary accommodation or social housing to homeowners. My mothers had either been working or studying prior to having their children. I found them through speaking at groups or they were directed to me by their medical professionals.

## How to use this book

The Guilt-Free Guide to Motherhood is a guide from pregnancy through to the early years of having a baby. It looks at the emotional and practical issues of being pregnant and raising a child but without giving exact advice because, as women, we are all different and so are our children. It aims to provide a perspective on motherhood and a space for you to consider how to be the best possible mother that you can be.

If you are pregnant then I recommend that you start at the beginning and work your way through until you have enough information. You can then dip in and out as appropriate. If you already have a baby, then you may want to start at the most relevant point to you now. However, I would suggest to everyone that they read the first chapter of the book as it is of value to all mothers.

Throughout The Guilt-Free Guide I discuss the aspects of motherhood that were important to my mothers and quote their actual words where possible. You will obviously not encounter every issue raised and while you will certainly find things that you can relate to, there will also be those that you can't. This is all as it should be. When you see the diverse range of motherhood experiences, it will free you up from attempting to be the same as everyone else, releasing you from the idea that there is a right way to be a mother.

If you are reading ahead, then there will be aspects of motherhood that you have not yet experienced and so you won't know how you will feel until you get there. Again, it is important to realise that some of my mothers had more challenging times than others. I have shared their tougher feelings, not to concern anyone, but to allow those aspects of motherhood to be acknowledged.

The Guilt-Free Guide to Motherhood was written based on women's experiences in the UK. Nevertheless, throughout the writing process I have spoken to mothers from other countries and cultures and found that there are many similarities, particularly around the emotions that motherhood brings up for us, which is the main emphasis of this book. There are, however, some terminology variations and differences in healthcare systems which might be useful to have explained if you are from another country. I refer to my women as 'Mothers' or 'Mums' because that is what I am used to. However, Mom, Mommy, Mamma are all interchangeable. In the UK, during labour we sometimes use Gas and Air (Entonox) to give mild pain relief which I am aware is not always available in other countries. A nappy is the same as a diaper or napkin. Tesco is a superstore. And lastly, here in the UK we have a state-funded healthcare system that sends midwives and health visitors into our homes. Health visitors are a special branch of nurses whose role is to give advice to mothers with children between birth and five.

# Chapter One
# THE JOURNEY TO MOTHERHOOD

Being pregnant for the first time is a profound phase in our lives. While we deal with the physical and emotional demands of pregnancy, we also begin to focus on the future; a future with our babies and a new stage in life. In the next chapters of this book I will join you in this, by exploring the breadth and depth of my new mums' experiences. We will look closely at the emotional impact of becoming a mum and how to navigate your way through the pressures of modern motherhood. But first we will take a look backwards at the feelings we experience on finding out we are pregnant and then to the all important expectations we have of motherhood.

## "I'm pregnant"

Finding out we are pregnant is a major event, when we realise that life is about to change in a big way. Every woman I interviewed, myself included, could recall the details of that moment. My mothers spoke of a range of feelings on finding out they were carrying a child, from joy to trepidation. We might expect only to be happy or excited, but for most of us it comes with other feelings too. There is often a potent mix of emotions, not only because we are facing the unknown, but also because we all journey to motherhood from our own unique places.

Within my group of women the surprise and immediate challenges were greatest for those who didn't plan to be pregnant. The emotional adjustments and preparation only began when the baby was already a reality, which can bring with it a great deal of uncertainty. Certainly, my mothers in this situation found that working out the practicalities and managing the impact on their relationship with the child's father brought added difficulty to the pregnancy, at least initially.

The majority of my mothers, however, had planned their pregnancies.

It would be easy to assume that we all come to motherhood with the same feelings because we have chosen to have a child, but this is simply not true. Even when we have arrived at the point of wanting a baby, our motivations and circumstances vary and so do our feelings. For some of my mothers, having a child felt like a natural progression in life because the desire to be a mum had always existed.

*"I felt ready to be a mum. I wanted to bring new life and raise them. I was extremely happy when I found out I was pregnant both times."*

*"It wasn't a conscious decision that I can ever remember making. I never wanted not to be a mother."*

This wish for a baby can become central to life. A number of my women spoke of a longing, so much so that it was painful to see other mums with their infants when they themselves were not pregnant. For these women, discovering they were carrying a child brought a deep sense of relief and satisfaction.

Alternatively, a number of my mothers were prompted to try for a baby by the growing sense that something was lacking in their lives. While for others, the desire came about through being happy or watching family and friends have children. Some of us are motivated to take action not by feeling ready necessarily, but by knowing that there is a greater risk of complications if we leave it beyond a certain age.

*"I'd always thought I'd want children and once I'd turned thirty and we'd been married a couple of years, we thought we'd better get on with it in case there were any problems."*

*"I knew I wanted children. I come from a large family myself. I was in my late thirties and the clock was ticking. I didn't feel quite ready but everyone said there is never a right time, so we went for it."*

The decision to have a child can be influenced by our experiences too. Women who have had a miscarriage, even if they did not plan the pregnancy, may find themselves afterwards longing for a child. A young woman pressured into having an abortion may then ache to have a baby she can keep. A woman who felt rejected by her parents may feel a need for a relationship of unconditional love. These circumstances can bring a whole host of feelings with them when we actually find ourselves pregnant.

The desire for children can also surface once we have worked through issues from our own childhood like watching our parents struggle, experiencing illness or disability within the family, or being unhappy ourselves as a child. Women like myself, who grew up not wanting kids, go through a huge shift in their image of themselves and their lives, making it highly likely that they will experience mixed feelings over the discovery of being pregnant.

*"I was very unsure if I wanted children. My husband was very keen. I was a little fed up with my job so I decided the time was right. My age was also a factor at thirty five... On learning I was pregnant I had mixed feelings [from] 'What have I done?' to 'This is exciting!'"*

Even within the group of women that I interviewed there were so many reasons for wanting a baby and this meant that there was also a range of emotions on finding out they were pregnant. There is certainly not a right way to feel on discovering we have a life growing within us. Some trepidation can be expected when heading into the unknown in any walk of life and it is no different with being a mother. Having complex emotions is not a reflection of how much we love or don't love our babies; instead they are a reflection of the varying paths that have led us to motherhood.

In fact, beyond our logical reasoning for wanting to be a mum there is much more to how we feel about motherhood than first meets the eye. To explore this we need to look further back in time.


## The Real Beginning

Most of us would consider the beginning to be conception (and great fun it is too) but the start of our journey to motherhood occurs way

3

before we actually get pregnant. Prior to egg meeting sperm, many factors have already influenced not only our decision to be a mother but also our attitudes and feelings towards motherhood. The process I am speaking of is called 'life'.

Interview after interview showed me that although as pregnant women we are going through the same physical process as each other and we have many shared experiences, we also arrive at this point from diverse places. Our feelings about having a baby are individual because we all have different expectations of motherhood. To understand how we differ so much we need to look back through our own lives.

By the time we are pregnant we have already absorbed so many ideas and feelings about what it means to be a mum. The two most powerful external contributors to these attitudes are our own upbringing and the messages we have picked up from society about being a woman and mother.

## Our Upbringing

Our closest insight into what motherhood entails comes from our own childhood. As a child we see before us our most intimate demonstration of what being a mother is. We learn deeply from the intense relationship we have with our own mums. Our relationships with our families set up a template for how we understand love and how secure we feel in the world. Through our childhood we develop our feelings and beliefs about ourselves and also plenty about being a parent. For example, someone who has had an unhappy upbringing will have a very different perception to someone who has been part of a content, loving family. Or, a woman who only saw her mother sacrifice for the sake of their family, would have a very different impression of what it is to be a mum compared to someone whose mother could be herself while raising children.

The circumstances of our upbringing and the feelings it produces in us have an impact on how we approach motherhood. We may assume that we will be just like our own mothers, we may desire to be completely different; either way we have gained our deepest knowledge from our family dynamic and this sets up many of our expectations, fears and hopes about becoming a mum.

### Social Ideas of Motherhood

Above and beyond our own parenting, we are also bombarded with society's ideas about being a mother. Adverts, photographs, artwork, television programmes and the prevailing social attitudes are everywhere, all the time. Magazines show photographs of celebrities looking well rested and beautiful, posing with their newborn babies. Television series show fictional families acting out a scenario designed to make us want to watch the programme again. The news discusses the latest hot topic on child rearing, usually in the most controversial way possible, pitching one side against another with little airtime for the middle ground. Underlying all of this are the prevailing social attitudes that each culture has to gender roles, which run through so many aspects of life that it can be hard to even notice them.

These representations of motherhood have elements of truth to them, yet what is not always apparent is that they are, more often than not, incomplete. They show one aspect of being a mum or sometimes either extreme. A perfect example is how, time after time, mothers are portrayed in terms of utter selflessness and complete devotion. The image of a devoted mother staring lovingly at her baby is seen so often, in many forms. Of course there is nothing wrong with this. The love and deep connection we feel for our infant is an essential part of raising a healthy child. However, it is not the whole truth but only one part of it.

Together, our own childhood and the social ideas of the time merge to give us an impression of what it is like to be a mother and an idea of what we 'should' be once we have children. Because of them, we expect certain things from our babies and certain things from ourselves.

## The Value Of Knowing Our Expectations

All woman approaching motherhood (and even those with a baby already) can benefit from considering their expectations. All of us have them; it is a part of being human. We think ahead and plan using the knowledge and beliefs we have. When we become a new mother, at least initially, our ideas of motherhood play a big part in whether we feel we are doing well enough. Making ourselves aware of our expectations and where they have come from helps us to acknowledge them for what they are: simply ideas that we have absorbed from elsewhere. In turn, this knowledge gives us flexibility. It is a bit like standing back to see what level we are setting the bar in a high jump. We may be setting it way too high or we may realise that we have planned a high jump, while actually long jump is more our style.

Take the example I used above of society's predominant message to women that mothers are supposed to be giving, loving and selfless. If we have unquestioningly absorbed this idea, then when we find ourselves with a new baby, exhausted, frustrated and humanly needing a break, it can wrongly feel as if we are failing.

Pregnancy is a perfect time to start to look at what we believe about motherhood. Considering what our own upbringing taught us and the social ideas that have had an impact on us, can be very useful. During pregnancy none of us are likely to know if we have set our bar too high or if we need to play the game in a different way, but we can log our influences so in the all new world of being a first-time mum we can use that awareness. This is not about doing anything or changing what you think but rather about acknowledging what has influenced your approach to motherhood.

Let's look at Beth as an example. Beth's expectations were that she would be a stay-at-home, highly child-focused mum who loved being with her children and creating a comfortable life for her family. Yet her actual experience was quite different. She didn't enjoy being at home all the time and wanted to go back to work. This made her feel like a failure. Beth's own mother had chosen to have lots of children and devoted her life to them. Once Beth understood that her concept of a good mother was based heavily on her own upbringing, it released her from the pressure of trying to be someone she was not. She could then freely assess what would make her the best mother she could be, which meant balancing work and time with her daughter. In letting go of her expectations, Beth found a much better balance by working a couple of mornings a week, which then allowed her to enjoy being at home with her daughter much more.

Knowing where our expectations come from can help us in pregnancy too, particularly if we have complex feelings around having a baby. We are expected, and therefore tend to expect of ourselves, to be only happy and joyful through our pregnancies. This sets off a pressure for us as mothers from the start (even before we have our babies) to not only behave but also feel a particular way. Yet, some of us learnt quite negative things about motherhood. I am a perfect example of this. Watching my mother struggle on a daily basis made me decide from a young age that I would never have children. A change of heart when I was thirty left me in the uncertain position of being pregnant after a lifelong fear of motherhood. But identifying the source of my concerns helped me place my fears where they belonged, the experience of someone else, namely my mother. When those anxieties reared up I could identify them as expectations based on my childhood and not necessarily on what the reality would be for me.

**A Good Mother**

Another way to think about expectations is to explore what we believe makes a good mum. This may be a general idea or a list of things a good mother would or would not do. Some of my women thought the perfect mum was someone who exclusively breastfeeds, makes all her baby's food and spends as much time as possible carrying her child. Others felt that it was a woman who could juggle a career and a baby. These are, of course, acceptable opinions to hold. They speak about our priorities and what we expect from ourselves. However, it is useful here to consider how flexible we are with these ideas. The problem comes when we link doing a particular thing or feeling a particular way with being successful. Beliefs like 'A good mother is always patient' for example or 'A good mother only feeds her baby home-made food' are very inflexible, allowing little room for manoeuvre on the days when everything gets a bit much. It is of course great to be patient and it is great to feed our babies food we have cooked. 'A good mother does her

7

best to be patient' or 'A good mother fits in what cooking she can' are much kinder and more flexible statements.

Some of my mums had huge lists of what they 'should' be doing. If we set the bar so high or have very fixed ideas about any topic, finding ourselves experiencing something quite different becomes challenging and we tend to blame ourselves. It is great to aspire to certain things in life. But allowing a little flexibility in our ideas of motherhood means that we can be kinder to ourselves if things don't go to plan. There are many ways to be a good mother. There are certainly things that we should not do. Anything that demeans or damages our children or ourselves is not okay. But within the range of loving parents, there are many ways to be successful. The reality of having a baby to care for will certainly be different from what we expect, because none of us can know motherhood before we experience it. Not one of my women found that motherhood was completely the way they had imagined. Nor did any feel that they were exactly the type of mother they had envisaged. We all have to adapt our ideas as we go along. Most of the women I spoke to found having a baby both harder and more wonderful than they could have imagined.

# Chapter Two

# PREGNANCY

# "I THINK MY LIFE IS ABOUT TO CHANGE"

So on to pregnancy itself and what a strange time it is. Our bodies go through dramatic changes and we attempt to plan for a future that will involve a baby but what it will actually be like, we can't really know. It can be exciting and scary, most likely it is a bit of both. In this chapter, we will look at some of the key pregnancy issues that my mums talked about and explore how they felt during their pregnancies. As you will see there is not one experience or a right way to feel; the process impacted my mums in varied ways both, physically and emotionally.

## Blooming Pregnancy - The Experience

As discussed in the previous chapter, we all come from unique places with differing attitudes towards motherhood so it's unsurprising that pregnancy evokes different emotions in us. Likewise, the experience varies massively depending on our circumstances and health. If we have relatively few symptoms, low stress levels, feel confident in our body and the health of our baby then it will be more enjoyable than if we feel ill or anxious.

The physical changes are, of course, so numerous and diverse that it is impossible to go into all of the symptoms my women had but there were some general themes to be seen.

Sickness was common but by no means universal. For most, it went after the first trimester but an unlucky few had it carry on. Exhaustion and being highly emotional were also noted in the early stages.

*"I couldn't believe how I could go from being really happy and then I just wanted to burst into tears."*

After the first trimester quite a few women spoke of having increased energy but in general the list of physical issues were less welcome. For some, feeling ill blunted their ability to enjoy pregnancy.

*"Each day I would just focus on getting through the day. I felt so awful, I couldn't be that excited or pleased about being pregnant."*

With the growing circumference of our stomach many more physical challenges crop up, which vary from person-to-person. But by the end, our size and general lack of mobility start to take their toll. In particular, immobility and working can become a real challenge. Tiredness kicks in because our bodies are being pushed to their limits and sleep becomes illusive, which had the majority of my mothers longing for it to be over by the final stages.

The idea that pregnancy leaves us feeling wonderful and glowing was not held up by my research. Only one woman among all of my mothers mentioned that she 'bloomed'. Most found the journey was not as clear cut as that, liking some aspects and disliking others.

Beyond the physical changes, pregnancy can alter how we feel about ourselves. Becoming bigger brought about widely differing feelings in my mothers. For some it was a pleasure to experience their bodies change so radically.

*"I liked my body a lot better when I was pregnant than I had at any other point in my life... Suddenly it was doing something amazing."*

There can be a joy in feeling a baby growing within us, knowing that we are creating a new life. However, this was not the case for everyone. For some, a lifetime of aiming to remain slim meant that the increasing size of their stomach made them feel 'fat', which led them to dislike what they saw and how they felt.

*"You just feel clumsy, you just feel big and clumsy."*

Pregnancy, while being the most womanly thing we can do, doesn't often feel feminine. Our culture links being slim, slender and graceful with femininity, which all go out the window as our bodies expand to accommodate a baby. Lifelong associations of this sort made it, for some, tough to feel attractive.

Carrying a child invariably has an impact on how we are with ourselves emotionally too. Pregnancy often makes us feel special. We are creating a new life and it is amazing. Our partners react to us differently; we all of a sudden have a shared purpose and hope for the future. Other people also start changing their behaviour, often being more caring.

*"I always had someone smile at me or someone asking me how many months I was. I loved the experience."*

*"People are so considerate and concerned and people come out of the woodwork who you never really thought would be that bothered."*

It is hard not to recognise that we are doing something important and of value. For many of my mothers, being pregnant meant that they had a reason to be nice to themselves, finding time to rest and relax when they normally wouldn't have.

*"I loved watching my bump grow. I enjoyed having permission to take time for myself to sit and read."*

One woman described it like being in her own bubble for nine months. Likewise for me, it was as if time took on a new meaning. I remember being at my kitchen table eating lunch slowly without feeling the need to get up or do anything else because my body was doing it for me. These feelings, whilst being common, were not universal. For some of my mothers it was important to continue functioning as close to normal as possible, perhaps supporting the belief that they could cope regardless.

Most of my women felt the significance of what they were doing and for a few this helped them instigate major life changes, like leaving behind damaging relationships. For these women, having more than themselves to think about made the choice to move towards a safe and respectful home life seem of greater value than ever before.

## Feelings in Pregnancy

Despite happily talking of all the challenges pregnancy brought, most of my mothers found these were eclipsed by the anticipation. All the aches and pains were temporary but the hope and excitement of a new child growing within them was the most lasting memory. Above and beyond the excitement were a number of other emotions that stood out for my mothers.

### "Will it be okay?"

All women have concerns about being pregnant. It is a unique and unknown experience, particularly first time round. We want to give birth to a happy and healthy baby and yet we are all too aware that there can be complications. The most feared is the potential for miscarriage. In the first trimester the majority of us have pregnancy symptoms but there are no reassuring kicks or a bump confirming the growing life within. These worries are completely normal and for many women they did not detract from their ability to recognise it as an amazing experience. They spoke of how surreal it was that, without any thought going into it, their bodies were just getting on with creating a new life. However, what is amazing for some of us, can be frightening for others.

*"I felt my body was totally out of control. I had no control over whether this baby was going to be born normal or whether I was going to be able to carry it for nine months. I had no control."*

For some women pregnancy touches an existing fear of not being in control. Those of my mothers who experienced this heightened level of anxiety had either a temperament or life experiences which meant that trusting that things would work out did not come easily. For most, this was helped by having a scan and later by feeling their baby move, while for others the concern remained.

> *"I worried a lot about the health of the baby even though everything was always okay according to scans and tests."*

Any previous miscarriages or scares within the pregnancy will undoubtedly heighten the fears that all women have of not being able to carry their child to term. Indeed, those who have miscarried in the past or had an abortion are starting from a point where they have been pregnant before. They will undoubtedly be reminded of their previous experience and any unresolved feelings may surface at this time.

For all of us pregnancy brings new levels of uncertainty and vulnerability into our lives. It is the start of an ongoing process of taking responsibility for another person's life. It is the flip side of love and something that we adjust to with time.

## Responsibility

When we are pregnant we start to become aware of the approaching responsibility that motherhood will bring. We are now inextricably tied to another human being. For most of us it starts out as a need to do the right thing for our babies. We eat the right foods and avoid anything that could be unhealthy. We plan and make adjustments to our homes and lifestyle, with the aim of providing the best possible environment for our newborns. We begin to consider our lives in a new way, becoming aware of our fragility and even mortality.

For the majority of my mothers this knowledge was on the periphery of their awareness. It felt as if their bodies were doing most of the work and the lack of conscious control limited that sense of responsibility. Most of my women said that they didn't really feel like a mother until their first child was actually born. Where this was very different was for the couples who had to make significant decisions about their babies in those nine months.

Pregnancy is the start of taking on another human being and although it may be sporadically daunting, the act of loving and caring for another person is empowering, bringing out the best in us.

**Guilt in Pregnancy**

It is easy to feel that we should enjoy pregnancy and to feel guilty if we don't, but the truth is that for some of us it is just not that enjoyable. Maybe the pregnancy itself is challenging or it brings up feelings from the past. Or it may just be that circumstances have created a whole heap of stress on top of being pregnant. It can be difficult for us to allow ourselves to feel unhappy or sad when we are pregnant because we just want to feel pleased and grateful.

It is easy to worry that a lack of enjoyment in pregnancy indicates that there could be a lack of love for our child once they are born. But this was not the case for my mothers. Those who didn't enjoy it still ended up loving their child.

If you are struggling emotionally then it may be worth talking to someone you trust. It can also be helpful to explore where these feelings may be coming from. Whatever the challenges are, acknowledging your emotions rather than fighting them is the best course of action. When we allow our feelings, we find that they naturally develop and we don't remain stuck with them.

Up until now I have been talking about the general experience of being pregnant, but there were also more specific issues that my mothers were confronted with.

# XY or XX and Does it Matter?

The majority of us can find out the sex of our baby if we choose to do so. Deciding whether to know in advance is a personal choice. Some mothers spoke of 'the not knowing' being the best part of the pregnancy. It added to the excitement and gave them a surprise at the end of labour. While others said that finding out their baby's sex helped them feel more connected to the life within them. There is no right or wrong answer to this one.

*"He was my little boy for quite a long time before he arrived."*

*"I can imagine me and my little lad at home doing our thing. I can imagine how my life is going to be. Why the sex of the child should change that, I don't know, but it does."*

For the majority, the gender of their babies didn't really concern them but I did come across a number of mothers that had an emotional attachment to having a child of a particular sex.

*"There was no way I could have a boy. I don't do blue and cars and bikes and things like that."*

This desire can be caused by a number of factors. There can be cultural bias where one sex is considered better than the other or families can have their own bias within them too. It can be down to familiarity; someone from an all girl family could be quite daunted by having a son. For other mothers there were deeper reasons for wanting their child to be a particular gender. One of my mums had a very bad relationship with her father and did not want a boy, while another mum had grown up with a sister with severe learning difficulties and found herself really wanting a son.

These feelings are not necessarily a cause for concern. If a particular gender is associated with certain problems then it can be easier to imagine a happy outcome with the opposite sex, no matter how much we logically understand that all we really want is a healthy baby. Both of my women gave birth to the gender they were concerned about and then went on to fall completely in love with their babies, regardless of their initial anxieties. Once their babies arrived they could no longer be associated with these other circumstances and their children became a wonderful learning experience for them.

If you do have a strong preference it might be helpful to consider what

underlying experiences are driving it. Is it cultural, is it a negative association or is it just a preference? Once we understand where our
anxieties come from then we can deal with them. Exploring why one
gender is better than the other by writing down your experiences of
and beliefs about males and females can also be really helpful. Write all
of it down without filtering the thoughts that come into your mind.
Only then, read back the points and see if they stand up to the light of
day. You can also ask others with children this question. What do you
love about having a boy/girl (whichever gender you are concerned
about)? You might be surprised by what they say.

## Antenatal Classes

Many of my mothers attended antenatal classes to get information
about childbirth and caring for their baby. Plenty found them helpful.
The knowledge they gained was mostly reassuring and it gave my
mums an opportunity to ask questions, alleviate concerns and meet
other people in the same situation. For many, the friendships made
within these groups became their support network once their baby was
born.

Some groups my mothers attended, however, seemed to be pushing a
very specific agenda rather than informing mums-to-be of their
options. These classes were reinforcing a narrow definition of what
makes a good mother, as if there is a 'right way' to have a baby, feed a
baby and so on. This feels very reassuring if all goes to plan but not if
we find ourselves having to make alternative choices. A few mothers
spoke of feeling alienated or even worse, as if they had failed by not
meeting the ideal criteria presented to them within their antenatal
group.

## Medical Support

The overall picture I gained from my mothers of their medical support
was generally a good one. The complaints they had were mainly minor.
Key frustrations were that there was a tendency for healthcare profes-

16

sionals to talk using medical terminology which made some of my mothers feel daunted, while others found it difficult to ask questions when faced with an apparently disinterested midwife or doctor.

Being pregnant for the first time is exciting but also emotional. So much is tied up with the life that we are carrying within us. We want our babies (and ourselves) to be strong and healthy. If all is going to plan then we find it easier to imagine the outcome we want. However, if there are concerns about the baby's health or our own, then this exciting journey can become a rather different experience. This is the time at which we need our medical professionals to help us the most, not just physically with the issues themselves but with the experience too. We need reassurance and help to understand our situation. Ideally, we need care that goes beyond the physical application of medicine and treats us as a person.

When there are complications and we find support is not forthcoming, or we are treated dismissively, it greatly adds to the stress. I imagine it can be all too easy for some medical professionals to be dismissive because for them the situation is not new. For us, however, it is new and all important; it is our baby and our body. We have not been in the situation before, we don't have a medical perspective unless it is explained to us and even then, when it is our baby and our body the thought that something could be wrong, is difficult.

Quite a number of women mentioned being unable to express what they wanted to within the medical environment. Intelligent, articulate women found themselves feeling unable to ask questions. There can be a variety of reasons that cause this difficulty. It may be that we don't find the medical staff approachable or that there is a palpable feeling of time pressure in the appointment. On a deeper level though, it can be to do with how we react to authority figures. As children we are brought up to behave and do what we are told by the adults (authority figures) around us. For many of us this continues through into adult life. When we are at an appointment with a doctor or midwife, particularly within a surgery or hospital, we find ourselves placing them in the role of the expert, which hopefully they are. This can, however, have the knock-on effect of putting us in a submissive position. We are being seen by someone in authority and we react accordingly.

In reality, the medical relationship should be a collaborative one. They have the expertise but we know ourselves. At best, we are treated with respect and listened to. Of course, this needs to be couched by saying that medical staff have pressures that we do not see and can have bad days just like us.

If appointments are difficult then there are things we can do to help ourselves. Firstly, it is important to know that we are allowed to ask questions and not know things. Some of my mothers spoke of feeling foolish for asking questions. Yet we can't know everything in life and everyone who finds themselves in a new situation will need to learn.

If you find it hard to express yourself well, writing a list of your key concerns and anything you want answered can be helpful. It can be so easy to get lost in the flow of the medical professional's procedures and difficult to interrupt without that reminder. If it helps, take someone with you that you trust. Let them know what you want to get from the appointment so they can step in if there are any omissions.

Of course, there are other sources of information available. Pregnancy books can be very informative. The internet may have information that can be helpful, but here we need to be cautious. There is no way of knowing how valid or up-to-date the information is on websites. Even where it is valid, there is the issue of too much information being a problem in itself. Websites or books for that matter, do not tailor their information to our needs or circumstances. A search online for the cause of a headache will inevitably lead us to an article listing every possibility right up to a brain tumour, even though it is highly unlikely.

If there are problems with your care then there is information out there about women's rights. One of my mothers founds the Association for Improvements in Maternity Services to be helpful in informing her what her rights were and what she could ask for. I have put a list of some support associations at the end of the book.

And lastly, if medical appointments still remain a real problem then it may be worth considering if it is triggering any deeper rooted feelings. One of my mothers found each appointment deeply stressful; they left her feeling unsettled and upset. For her it brought up her childhood experiences of being in hospital. Medical settings distressed her and this made the pregnancy and birth particularly difficult. If emotional issues from the past are surfacing then it can be useful to talk to someone or to write down how you feel. Writing down the emotions created in the present and then the emotions experienced in the past can help us see the link between the two and so view it from another vantage point.

## Mental Health in Pregnancy

Mental health problems are more common than most people think. It is estimated that ten to fifteen percent of women do have some issues during pregnancy, the most common being depression and anxiety. For some, it is a resurfacing of an existing mental health issue, whereas for others it is their first experience.

Any mental health conditions can occur during pregnancy as at any other time. However, there are some that relate specifically to being pregnant. Postnatal Depression is most commonly associated with after having had a baby but it can start during pregnancy itself. There is also Perinatal or Prenatal Obsessive Compulsive Disorder. This is a condition where women feel very anxious, with particular concerns about their babies being harmed or contaminated. It differs from the occasional concerns that all mothers have about the health of their unborn child. These feelings are overwhelming and cause the mother-to-be to spend a significant amount of time on behaviours designed to alleviate her fears. An example would be overly limiting the types of food eaten or washing and cleaning excessively.

The Royal College of Psychiatrists suggests that anyone with a severe illness, anyone who has had treatment from mental health services, anyone who has had Postpartum Psychosis or severe Postnatal Depression, those with severe anxiety disorders and those with an eating disorder receive advice during their pregnancies, even if they feel well. I have referenced some information sources at the end of this book, which go into more depth.

If you have suffered mental health disorders before then it is important to discuss this with your medical professionals. Any medication also needs to be taken into account. The best approach to dealing with your issues will depend on how severe your problems have been.

Within my group of women, there were those who had had mental health problems in the past, who knew the warning signs and were versed in where to get help and there were also those who experienced issues during their pregnancy for the first time.

If you feel that you are struggling emotionally with pregnancy then it is worth talking to someone. Often sharing anxieties with supportive people helps them to lift. It may be that this is not enough, in which case talk to your doctor or a counsellor; they will be best able to discuss your personal circumstances and point you in the right direction.

## End of Pregnancy

One theme that was almost universal was that by the end of pregnancy we are really tired of it and just want to get on with having our child. Being huge, ungainly, symptom-ridden and not sleeping all takes its toll on us. Even those who had their babies on time wanted it over with. Those who were late, generally got positively cranky.

The waiting can feel endless and while it can seem like it will go on forever the truth is that it doesn't. Being pregnant is finite. Whether we have our baby early or two weeks late, it will happen.

# Chapter Three
# THE BIG EVENT
# BIRTH & MEETING OUR BABY

Giving birth is a profound time for every mother. The culmination of the previous nine months comes to a head and our bodies take over. We give ourselves over to our physiology and ride the waves of labour, with whatever that brings.

It is difficult to write about the emotional impact of childbirth for women who have never experienced it. Each person has such different responses and it is one of those events where words always fall short. Indeed, the stories of the women I interviewed were as varied and unique as they were. There were long labours, short ones, caesarean sections (planned and emergency), births with medical complications, water births and one that went exactly to plan. Some found it amazing, whereas others didn't. The only common thread in each mother's story was how significant an event it was. The women I interviewed wanted to talk about it because no matter what happened, the experience was extremely profound.

Before going into what my mothers wanted you to know about the birth experience, I first want to explore a very significant aspect that many of my mums realised influenced how they felt about the birth of their babies: that of making a birth plan.

## Planning a Birth

Many of us, when we are pregnant, make a birth plan. It is a statement of our preferences on topics like what pain relief we want, where we want to have our baby, how we feel about medical intervention and what we would like to happen immediately afterwards. We have the right to change our minds at any time, but a birth plan is meant to be a reference point for our medical staff so they can understand our wishes.

Birth plans were a hot topic for my mothers. Now, before I go into their opinion of them I will first say what benefits they have. Pre-planning gives us the opportunity to educate ourselves on all the possibilities facing us as we approach the birth of our baby. In compiling a birth plan we get to understand the choices we may be asked to make and it helps us decide what is important to us personally. Inherent in this process is the understanding that as pregnant women we have the right to decide what happens to us and our bodies before, during and after we have our babies; a point that has all too often been overlooked in the past with the medicalisation of childbirth.

However, the one message that almost all of my mothers wanted to share with you as mums-to-be was not to place too much emphasis on the plan.

*"Just plan to get your baby out safely whatever that means. That is the most important thing. The birth never goes as you planned it anyway."*

And the reason? Well the births my women had planned for over the months did not transpire, leaving many feeling disappointed or worse, as if they had failed. Indeed, only one of my mothers had the birth she imagined. For many of my women the process of making a birth plan made them envisage a very specific course of events which belied the reality, that childbirth is a fluid experience that progresses in its own way and not to any predefined specifications.

For example, a number of my mothers who planned a birth with no drugs (other than gas and air) found that their decision altered once they were in labour. They understandably wanted to make the best choice for their babies and avoid some of the risks associated with pain relief but when it came to it they changed their minds, leaving a number feeling weak.

These women did not meet their own expectations and so some felt like they had failed. Similarly, other mothers felt a failure after having a caesarean section.

*"I felt a bit of a failure for not having given birth naturally and I still do, like it's this experience I missed out on. It's stupid really. I'd love to say I was one of those people that just had gas and air and toughed it out."*

The birth of our baby is not something we can plan with any certainty because the variables are enormous. What we really need is our babies and ourselves to come through it as healthy as possible and there are many ways to do that. The best scenario is that we are fully informed about our options, that we know our rights and that we are flexible about how our child comes into the world. The more fixed an idea we have about what 'should' happen, the more scope there is for the actual birth to be a disappointment or for us to disappoint ourselves. You are, of course, free to have your own ideals and aspirations. However, it may be that you change your mind or necessity dictates an alternative path, none of which makes you less successful at childbirth.

This doesn't mean that a birth plan has no value. Doing it brings about an awareness of the issues we may face, our priorities and also our rights. In my mind, they are a useful tool as long as they are put into perspective. Likewise, my mothers were not against the plans altogether but they found that creating a very precise idea of what they wanted was counter-productive to them feeling satisfied with the birth afterwards.

## Natural childbirth
One possible reason that pain relief and caesarean sections provoked feelings of failure or weakness in some (not all) of my mothers, may have very little to do with the making of a birth plan and more to do with the current childbirth conversation.

As a kickback from the over medicalising of childbirth and loss of women's autonomy there has been a push towards seeing childbirth as a natural process, which of course it is. But that has spilled over, at times, into the unspoken idea that the *best* type of birth is a natural one, as if natural is always better and even makes us better mothers. I have no argument with anyone who chooses to do things naturally. Like many of my mothers I aspired to have a birth with minimal intervention. I only take issue with the correlation between this and being a good mother or a better mother.

The harder we hold onto an idea that there is a good or bad way to have a baby, the harder it might be to accept the reality. The reality is that as mothers we get on with the situation we are given and do what is in the best interests of ourselves and our babies.

Another kickback from the natural conversation is that the very word 'natural' is frequently associated with 'gentle' and 'easy'. But childbirth is a challenging time for our bodies. Some of my mothers were surprised by their reactions to giving birth. They expected it to be easier because it is a natural process.

So, while I don't want you to mistake my approach as being pro-pain relief or pro-caesarean or anti-birth plans, I am suggesting, after the many conversations with my mothers, that we can be kind to ourselves. We do this by being flexible, allowing ourselves to change our minds and giving ourselves the freedom to make choices as the event unfolds.

## Giving Birth

With a baby growing in our womb there is one unavoidable event on the horizon: childbirth. We all have our preconceived ideas of what this will mean and without a doubt we will have mixed feelings, wondering what it will be like and how it will go. It is exciting to know that we will meet our baby but scary to face the unknown. Before our first labour we have no point of reference. We can listen to other women's stories and research the topic but there are so many variables that it is impossible to tell what it will be like for us personally.

At this point I could go into the birth stories of my mothers in great depth but, to be honest, I doubt its value in preparing anyone for labour. Some of my mothers found hearing about childbirth helpful and others didn't. For many it still gave the wrong impression and for some it just created anxiety. However, from talking to all my mothers there were things that they either wished they had known or that they felt were helpful when approaching childbirth for the first time.

## Ask for what you want

Most of us give birth in a medical environment or at least with medical help. This can at once be reassuring and quite disempowering. We feel reassured by having people with expertise around but at the same time we don't feel in control. The hospital environment in particular can make it hard to say what it is that we need. Most of my mothers felt less assertive than usual, even those who were used to medical settings. As I have said before, the more we have been taught to defer to others if we feel they have more authority than us, the more difficult it can be to say what it is that we want. And at a time when we feel vulnerable, this can be magnified. But what my mothers wanted you to know is that you may not have all the knowledge and you certainly do have to rely on the professionals, but you also have the right to say what you feel and ask for what you want.

## You are the expert on you

This follows on from my mothers' previous point. While it is good to take guidance from those with expertise it is also important to keep in mind that we are the experts on ourselves. No one else knows you or how you feel.

## There are no stupid questions

Some of my mums held back on asking questions which, with hind-sight, they wished they had asked because they would have felt better. A lack of knowledge is just that, a lack of knowledge. As human beings we can't know everything and we are not supposed to. Asking questions of medical staff is completely appropriate. They are there to support us and part of that is to give us the information that we need.

## *Know your rights*

Knowing what our rights are can help us as we receive medical support during childbirth. Within my group of women this was useful for many, but none more so than for those who found the medical environment made them feel anxious or powerless. For one mum, knowing her rights completely transformed her feelings about childbirth. The most helpful piece of information for this mum was that we, as women, are able to make choices about our own pregnancy and childbirth, even where our caregivers do not agree. This one bit of information empowered her and helped her feel more in control. There are, of course, other rights. We have a right to receive safe and appropriate maternity care that respects our fundamental human dignity and we also have a right to privacy and confidentiality, as well as equality and freedom from discrimination. There are details of support organisations with more information listed at the back of the book.

## *Have support*

During childbirth we are both powerful and vulnerable. Powerful because we are the centre of life-giving but vulnerable because we are so reliant on others. Having trusted support through the process helps immeasurably. Sharing the experience with someone we know and who knows us is not only reassuring but they can become another line of communication between us and those assisting with the birth. All my mothers had support and they spoke of it as invaluable. If there is a question over whether your designated person will be available, have someone else on standby.

## *Trust yourself*

We can do ourselves a disservice when we over-think because we just can't work out all the permutations of life in general. Trusting ourselves and our ability to cope with what life throws at us is a great life tool. It is no different with childbirth. It is important to know that you will cope with what ever happens. It may not be what you expected, it may be everything you hoped for, most likely somewhere in-between. However it transpires, you will get through it. At the end you will have achieved something both profound and wonderful.

Labour sweeps us along with it, we get carried with the tide of our body's process and the intense parts of childbirth leave little room for anything else. No matter how it goes, be kind to yourself. Whether or not it is what you thought it would be, know that you are doing it. Likewise, afterwards it is so important to acknowledge the magnitude of what you have done. It may be natural and done throughout history but it is still amazing, every single time.

Being gentle with ourselves is incredibly important during and after childbirth. This is even more the case when we have had a demanding birth. All of us hope for an easy delivery. Sometimes however, it just doesn't go like that. In the moment we all deal with what happens. But after a challenging birth it is even more important to be kind to ourselves and avoid the temptation to make comparisons between ourselves and others. Accepting our feelings is the best way to move through them. When we have been distressed by childbirth, discussing what happened with medical staff can be helpful. We gain a perspective that we did not have at the time. Birth is all consuming and the events can all be a bit of a blur, which can leave us wondering and questioning ourselves.

As with all life experiences, we learn and grow from having our babies whether it is what we expected or not. For all of us, the birth of our children is a profound and powerful time, one that we can be sure we will never forget.

## Meeting Our Babies

During pregnancy all of us think about the moment of meeting our babies for the first time. Most of us tend to assume that we will be overwhelmed by love for our newborns the instant we see them and indeed this is what many of my mothers experienced.

> *"The rush of love just blew me away, I couldn't believe it. I just wanted to wrap him up and protect him."*

*"The love was there instantly... I kept telling myself 'She's mine'."*

*"I loved him and looked forward to getting to know him. I was proud of him too. He was an easy baby to carry and give birth to."*

For these mothers meeting their babies was everything they expected, in many cases more. The love they felt was instant and powerful.

If, however, we are not overcome with love in those first moments it can be quite disconcerting or even worrying. Nevertheless, feeling an instant connection was by no means universal, with over a third of my women not experiencing it that way. Some spoke of feeling something but not the intense love they had expected, whereas others admitted that they felt very little.

*"I'm not going to say I loved her instantly. I did love her. It was the most surreal feeling ever."*

This caused a range of emotions, from those who just trusted that their feelings would grow and evolve to those that worried that it was a sign that they might not bond with their babies.

There are, of course, many factors that contribute to our feelings when we meet our baby. A difficult birth, having a caesarean section, general exhaustion, illness or just being uncertain all have an effect on that first meeting.

*"I can't remember feeling anything much, partly because I was spaced out on pethidine. I think I was quite pleased with her. It is all a bit of a blur"*

For me, being generally nervous of babies and fairly convinced I was having a girl, my first thought on being handed a baby boy was, 'I don't know you.' It was intense; a moment in time I will never forget, but I felt curiosity rather than overwhelming love. I remember being very interested in him, while also being scared about managing a tiny baby.

28

# Bonding - A Moment in Time or a Journey?

So much emphasis on the importance of bonding had given many of my mothers the wrong impression. Plenty had the idea that bonding with our baby happens straightaway; we give birth and we bond.

Many of my mums feared there was something wrong when they didn't have that instant or overpowering reaction to their newborn. It is, of course, essential for a baby to have a mother who is tuned into them and their needs. But the idea that there is this moment in time when a bond is created is simply not true. The reality is that bonding with our child is a process, like building any new relationship. For all of us, the feelings that we have for our children grow and evolve. Caring for our babies in itself fosters the love that we have for them. The majority of my women who didn't feel it right away discovered that the connection began to emerge with time.

> *"I didn't feel much of a bond at all, just as if someone had given me a baby and I had to look after it. Of course, that all changed completely within a few weeks."*

There was also a fear among some of my mothers who were unable to be with their babies straightaway that it would have a long-term impact on their ability to connect with their infants.

> *"I didn't get to hold her for about an hour, which is nothing in the scheme of things. But when you have spent your whole pregnancy reading about how skin-to-skin contact is so important and you must have your baby put on to your tummy as soon as it's born I thought 'Oh no, I am not going to bond with this baby!'"*

We know that immediate skin-to-skin contact with the mother is a really good thing, however, some of my mums or their babies required medical intervention so it was just not possible. Despite these real fears over there being damage to the relationship between them and their babies, by the time I was interviewing my mothers, none of them felt that they hadn't connected successfully with their child.

Worries about bonding were common amongst my mothers. Some felt that initially they should not even want to step away from their newborns to have a shower. However, time dispelled these concerns. Of course, if we don't feel a connection to our child over time then it needs to be looked into. Anyone who doesn't feel a bond with their baby would be best to talk to their doctor, health visitor or a therapist to explore what might be going on.

The essence of what my mothers wanted other expectant women to know was that the birth of our babies cannot be pre-defined before it happens and that it's certainly not helpful to judge it afterwards. It is what it is and we all do our best. Childbirth is a part of our journey with our babies but it does not define how the rest of the journey will be. These quotes sum up the the key points my mothers made.

*"Be realistic in your expectations. Everything and everyone led me to believe that nine out of ten births were easy and as planned. That doesn't seem to be the reality. Keep your ideal birth in mind but be prepared."*

*"Don't expect too much of the birth and try to put it behind you. It doesn't matter once it is over (Great advice, I need to take it myself). Don't worry if you don't feel you have bonded instantly. It takes a while."*

*"Don't have too many expectations; just go along with it because you don't know how you're going to be."*

# Chapter Four
## LET'S GET PRACTICAL
## COPING WITH A NEW BABY

The moment has arrived, the one we have been waiting for yet couldn't quite imagine. We have our newborns and our life with them begins, but what now? There is no manual that comes with each baby giving us guidelines right for our specific child. There are many practical skills that we have to learn but what is most noticeable, in this early stage, is all the emotions that we experience as part of becoming a mother.

### Emotions in the First Weeks

I would love to say that my women found early motherhood easy and blissful but they didn't. Now I am not aiming to put anyone off. Rather, I want to relay the truth of what my mothers told me so that you know what to expect. Their reality was a whole roller-coaster of diverse and often conflicting but, most notably, intense emotions. Here is what they listed...

| | | |
|---|---|---|
| *Incredulous* | *Energetic* | *In love* |
| *Overwhelmed* | *Stunned* | *Sore* |
| *Immobile* | *Grateful* | *Fearful* |
| *Proud* | *Nervous* | *Battered* |
| *Drained* | *Happy* | *Elated* |
| *Tired* | *Anxious* | *Weak* |

Immediately after having our babies can be overwhelming because we have so many new feelings. We have a newborn, which is at once both amazing and scary. We feel deeply protective and so, in many ways, more vulnerable. At the same time, we are dealing with the after-effects of childbirth and the new effects of caring for a baby. When asked what was the hardest time, many of my mothers said it was this first bit.

*"I now look back and feel that the first few weeks were the hardest, most frightening time of my life."*

*"Just after birth [was the hardest time]: the sleep deprivation, breastfeeding and the general demanding nature of newborns."*

*"You just wonder what the hell has happened to your life for the first couple of months."*

Of course, our initial experience will be greatly effected by our personal circumstances, particularly the birth and our physical and emotional health. A challenging labour or being unwell, are bound to make those first few days or weeks more difficult. But even when everything goes to plan we don't necessarily bounce back and feel on top form. Giving birth is a massive physical task and it needs to be respected as such. One of my mothers wanted to send a message to all other new mums...

*"Be warned beforehand that you may not feel yourself and this is all normal."*

Having said all of that, some women spoke of an elation and energy after having their baby, which helped them power through the new challenges.

*"The energy buzz got me through."*

*"The first day I felt quite elated and well physically. The following days after I remember feeling more tired."*

*"I remember feeling tired but elated at the same time. It's that real adrenalin rush. You're living off no sleep but you're so happy. The first few weeks it was great but then I think the novelty wears off a bit and the first six weeks are really tough."*

*"I felt an immense amount of energy for weeks, which helped with the sleepless nights. The responsibility to Rosa was (and still is) intense."*

32

However we are physically, emotionally we have to face a whole new and unknown situation, which can leave us feeling vulnerable and unsure at times. There are numerous different responsibilities and demands in having a completely dependent child and that in itself brings up many emotions.

> *"I was petrified I was going to hurt him in the first twenty-four hours. Thinking 'He is so small. What if I break him?' "*

> *"I felt like my head was everywhere and I didn't know this little bundle who was very unpredictable."*

As the women above attest to, these first days can be bewildering. We have yet to find our feet as mothers and build our confidence. We don't know exactly what to do because we have never been in the situation before. We don't yet know our baby and they are not used to us or being out in the world. Finding this disconcerting is entirely normal. There are, of course, many wonderful emotions that come with having our new baby. Most of us expect to feel joy and happiness but what took my mums by surprise was the variety and intensity of emotion and how tough it can feel at times.

One thing that many mothers experience soon after labour is the 'baby blues'. We may feel low, tearful, irritable, depressed or anxious. I looked into estimates for how many women go through it and I found numbers ranging from over fifty percent and up to eighty percent. Clearly this is quite a common feature of having a baby. The baby blues is thought to be caused by hormonal fluctuations after giving birth and it could be one of the reasons that the early stages provoke such powerful emotions. It tends to start a few days after childbirth and usually settles down by day ten.

Interestingly, the majority of my mothers did not mention the baby blues. Their feelings in those early days were so complex that identifying whether the cause of their emotions was down to the baby blues or all the other changes they were experiencing, was not high on their list of priorities. Yet as we can see from above, the highs and lows at this time can be quite marked and hormonal fluctuations are likely to play their part.

It is essential with a new baby to be really kind to yourself and get as much support as you can from other people. Childbirth and having a newborn is a potent combination. If you have help, then this is the time to do as little as possible and just focus on yourself and your baby. Remember, there is no right way to feel. Some of it might be great, some of it might be tough and that is all normal.

Of course, in these early days what is happening, often completely without our awareness, is that we are learning. We are learning to read our babies and gaining insight into what works for them. At the same time, our babies are learning about being in the big wide world too. Our feelings in this stage are very fluid; there are naturally ups and downs. There are many wondrous things about having a new baby and, with the stakes so high, there are scary elements too. This invariably settles down as we become more accustomed to motherhood and our baby becomes more familiar with life outside the womb.

When we know that other mothers experience a similar roller-coaster of emotions it can allow us to accept our feelings and not judge them. However, if after a few weeks things don't start to feel somewhat better, then it would be worth discussing your feelings with your health visitor or doctor.

## Sleep Glorious Sleep

Sleep is a big challenge for parents in the early part of their babies lives. Moving to a twenty-four hour day, being woken repeatedly for feeds, is not easy. Knowing that we might be needed at anytime takes getting used to. Likewise, having a baby sleeping right next to us can also take some adjustment. For me as a light sleeper, I found that to start with I would hear every breath, gurgle and snort my son made, which he did most of the night. Laying awake I kept wishing for quiet so I could sleep, but then when there was silence I immediately wondered if he was alright, as he was normally so noisy.

The sleep changes are one of those aspects of motherhood that just needs to be gone through. In an ideal world we would sleep whenever possible. This is advice you will have heard over and over again and it sounded like a joke to some mums who found snoozing impossible in the day. Being told to ignore the housework and lay down is great advice to some and impossible advice to others. Ultimately, as a new mum we need to find our own way to be mindful of our needs as well as our baby's. With time, however, things begin to change for our little ones who at some point stretch out their sleep times and begin to know night from day. I talk in much more depth about this topic in Chapter Five in the section on Exhaustion.

## Visitors and Help

One of the things we all have with a newborn, is visitors. It can be so wonderful to share our baby with those that love and care for us. Often it is an unexpected bonus to experience the pleasure that our infant brings to others and, at the same time, get much needed support. Other experienced mothers now become invaluable and anyone who will take our baby for a spell or help out while we rest, is a blessing. The top tip from many of my mothers was to make use of any visitors. Motherhood is not a self-sufficiency competition. It is about managing long-term in the best way that we can.

*"Let people help you and don't feel guilty about resting. Lean on all the people who are there to support you as much as possible and don't be afraid to ask for help."*

*"If someone offers help, accept it and don't try to be a superhuman. And if people don't offer help, ask for it."*

*"If you have got family and friends coming round, instead of them seeing the baby, actually have them make a cup of tea or help with the vacuuming."*

*"If your partner is not supportive practically, try and get help if you can with cleaning, ironing etc."*

*"If you have got family around, use them. If you have got friends around use them… You do feel guilty. You feel like you should be doing it all yourself, which is really silly."*

*"Do ask for help and don't feel like you have to do it all. Lean on other people a little bit. But also make sure you have time to yourself."*

Getting help and sharing in the excitement of a new baby can be such a special time. Yet, for some of my mothers there was a significant down side to all the family and friends coming over. The demands placed on them by the visitors became a pressure that hindered rather than helped. One of my mums had ten people in the first day and then a constant stream from then on, not leaving anytime for herself, her partner and her baby. Another found that trying to keep everyone who was visiting happy was adding to her exhaustion.

*"Some days I'd have three or four lots of visitors and that would be all day long and I would be exhausted and thinking 'Where is my time?' I was trying to please everybody rather than putting myself first."*

Once we are mothers our priorities need to change. We will not be able to please everyone as much as we used to. For some of my mothers learning to create boundaries, allowing time and space for themselves and their baby, became an important learning curve. One such mum, in the end, asked for one day a week with no one coming to the house.

For many of us though there are limits to the amount of help available. Working partners and families often mean that there is less than we would like. If the support you are getting is not what you need then think about what would make the difference. Often it is not huge changes that are required but little things like getting a visitor to make the tea or our partner to take over so we can have a thirty minute bath.

Earlier I said that motherhood was not a self-sufficiency contest and the general consensus from my women is to accept as much help as possible. However, a few of my mothers had a great deal of support and while sounding ideal, it actually began to undermine their confidence.

In order to feel capable as a mother we need to know that we can cope with enough of the tasks required of us. So for these women, beginning to step away from the support became important. As my mothers in this situation explained, this can be a bit of an emotional minefield because of the potential to offend those who are helping. Despite this, they gradually learnt to take back one thing at a time, stepping in to say "I will do that" whenever they could.

## Midwives

Midwives that visit in the weeks after the birth can be really helpful. A good midwife should be able to fill the gaps in our knowledge. They can bestow pieces of information that make a huge difference and inform us of what we are already doing well, to help us grow in confidence. Mine saw me jumping up every time my son made a sound. She gently explained that not every noise he made meant there was a problem and that if I listened, I would hear the difference. It was so simple. Once she said it, I knew she was right. That single bit of advice helped me relax.

The majority of my mothers found their midwife supportive, but not all of them. At this stage it can be hard to feel that we know anything, but it is also important to remember that we won't always get the right advice. A number of my mothers spoke of feeling that the guidance they received was a 'one-size-fits-all' answer, rather than something that was appropriate to them and their baby. One thing quite a few of my mothers wanted new mums to know was that we do not have to accept information offered to us. We can listen but we need to make up our own minds. One mum summed it up by saying...

> *"Listen to what they say, take it on board and use it or not.*
> *Don't think that everything they say is correct."*

## Coping Alone

Initially, being left alone with our babies can be quite daunting. There is so much to learn, so much to do and we have not yet developed our confidence as mothers. For most women the first time they experience coping entirely alone is when their partner goes back to work. Others that had family staying only face it when they leave. No matter when it happens, all of us have that day where suddenly it is down to us alone.

Quite a few of my mothers found that mastering the baby equipment was essential to their confidence in managing by themselves. I certainly remember only too well the horrors of the baby car seat. It seemed so complicated at the time and the combination of back pain and being bent over in the car trying to fathom exactly which slots to use, was not my idea of fun. This and a lack of sleep had me holding back a few choice words. Other mothers spoke of the very good, but often complex, baby travel systems being their nemesis. Being out with our newborns and finding ourselves unable to collapse a buggy, in order to put it in the back of the car, can be really upsetting on only a few hours sleep.

However, once we have worked out the mechanics of the baby paraphernalia then the world begins to open up to us. Possibilities for going out bring a new sort of independence to our life with our baby.

Going out alone the first few times is an enormous task. We feel more vulnerable and protective and in a practical sense, there is so much to think about.

*"I remember the first time going to the supermarket on my own thinking 'How am I going to cope? How am I going to cope?' It seems ridiculous now."*

*"The first time I took him out, the first couple of times actually, I was suspicious of everybody and I couldn't relax and I was forcing myself out because I felt it was good for me but I didn't want to be out."*

Leaving the house is like embarking on an expedition. Popping to the shops with just money and a phone, is a thing of the past. There are so many things to remember but like the equipment, we soon learn what we need and create systems for making sure we have it all with us. All of my mums talked about going out alone with their baby for the first time as a major event. Some started small and headed for the nearest shop or park. Others went the whole hog to convince themselves they could manage, going to town or out for a entire afternoon. Once we have mastered being out with our babies though, we begin to feel much more confident as mothers. As one of my new mums said with great pride...

*"Where ever we want to go and what ever we want to do,*
*we can do it. There is nothing stopping us now."*

In order to gain confidence it is important to realise that motherhood is an art form. There is not one way to go about it. There will be ups and downs, days when you feel you can't do it and others where it feels like you are getting the hang of things. There will be days when you wonder what you have done to your life and days when everything seems just wonderful. Knowing that every mother has bad times and really feels like she doesn't know what she is doing is important because then we understand that it is not just 'us' doing something wrong or failing where others manage fine.

## "A Mother! Who, Me?"

A number of my women mentioned how strange it felt to be a mother. We may have a baby suddenly but our feelings about ourselves and our role in life sometimes take longer to adjust.

*"I don't feel any different you see. I still feel like he's on loan and I'm*
*not really his mum. It feels all a bit fake. It hasn't really sunk in.*
*I feel like I am too young to have a baby, which is ridiculous*
*because I am almost classed as an older mother."*

*"[It was] a bit surreal really. It's the strangest thing I've ever gone*
*through. [Motherhood is] really pleasant. I'd say it's a pleasant*
*experience and one of the best things I have ever done.*
*One of the hardest things as well."*

This early stage of motherhood is a huge life change. For most of us it is the biggest alteration we will have to our lives. We move from a place where we care for ourselves to one where we have a dependent person in our charge. Subsequent children add to our workload but it doesn't compare with the upheaval of our first. Such a huge change can be both difficult and exciting. The one thing that is certain (yet it often doesn't feel like it at the time) is that it won't be like it forever. Babies change and grow and so do we as mothers.

*"Take each hour as it comes and know that it really does get easier."*

## The New Meaning to Time

Our society places a high emphasis on being in control of our lives; self determination is the name of the game. In order to be successful there is this idea that we always need to know where we are going and what we are doing. As part of education and then a job, most of us spend much of our lives working to targets and being assessed. Motherhood has none of this. We enter a much more vague world that holds to no particular pattern (at least to begin with) and if we do create any sort of schedule, it is forever changing because our babies change. There are no specific targets or deadlines, there are just days of seeing to our child. We may have a lot to do, but there is little to show for it.

*"You can spend a whole day just looking after a baby*
*and not get a chance to do anything else at all."*

It can be frustrating to not be able to get round to the tasks that we need to. Before having a baby it would be ridiculous to think that it could take all day to have a shower and get a sink load of dishes washed. But that is often how it is once we have children, somedays more so than others. Constant carrying, cuddling, feeding and chan-ging mean that we can, at times, feel very unproductive. I remember being amazed at how little I could do on some days and then on others feeling like a 'super-mum' because I would cook and clean while being fully showered and dressed. I soon realised that the change was not with me but with my son. If he was content then I could get on with the other tasks of motherhood. If he wasn't, well then I just couldn't, no matter how much I wanted to.

Pregnancy and birth are finite and there is a natural limit to the time that they will take. Whereas, the baby stage, with its inherent lack of structure, can feel endless. With hindsight this period in our lives is actually quite short as our babies grow so quickly. But we don't have hindsight in the moment and in the twenty-four hour days of being a new mum there is not much to mark the passing of the hours, days and even weeks.

It is important to keep in mind that even if it feels that we are getting very little done, the truth is the opposite. Raising a child is not about the tasks that we do or how well we keep the house but it is about being present and responding to them. A baby doesn't care if the house is tidy or we have our makeup on. What it does know is if its needs are being met. The sometimes endless undefined days can easily hide the truth which is that we are the most powerful influence in another human's development. They already have their own personality but we are helping to form the person they will become and how they will feel about themselves. What an amazing thing that is.

## Parent and Baby Groups

There are all kinds of groups out there for families and their babies. There are usually local meet-up groups and also many interactive classes involving an activity like baby yoga or music. For many of my mums, getting out to meet other people in the same situation as them was invaluable. Joining a group provided some structure to their lives and got them out of the house into a child-friendly environment. Through conversations with other mothers, they realised they were not alone in experiencing the highs and lows of raising a child.

There were varying opinions among my mothers about what type of group was best. Some found certain groups too prescriptive. Others found the socialising difficult in mother and baby settings, preferring interactive classes where there were other activities going on.

*"I didn't enjoy the mum and baby groups run by the health visitors. They were just a time to drink tea and boast about whose baby is best while they are left to play on the floor. I prefer interactive sessions like yoga."*

*"Mother and toddler groups are a godsend."*

*"I was sceptical about this [interactive baby groups] before I had Kieran but they have been great to provide structure, discuss problems with other mums, realising you are not the only one. And they get you out."*

*"I've found toddler groups a bit harder [than interactive baby groups] because I'm shy of going into a crowd and talking to people."*

For me, my local groups were a life saver. Exhaustion and a general feeling that I didn't completely know what I was doing made it hard to head into a new social situation. However, I went and found that after the first few weeks I began to see familiar faces and friendships ensued. When I eventually did get a few other mothers that became closer friends, it was such a relief. We would talk baby, share our experiences, frustrations, disasters and happy times. We learnt from each other, consoled each other and laughed together.

The main message from my mothers about these groups, apart from them being really good, was to persevere in finding ones that work for you. It can take a little experimentation but it is well worth it in the long run.

## Social Life

Having a baby makes an inevitable impact on our social life primarily because we no longer have the time we did but also because, as all of my mothers pointed out, our priorities change once we have a child in our lives.

My women generally spoke of feeling more in tune with friends that already had children. Some of my mothers spoke about friendships petering out where the friend didn't have or want kids. Our lives have taken such a distinct change in direction that it can be hard to keep up with (or even feel connected to) people who don't share the same responsibilities we do.

*"Certain childless friends don't ask to see you as much. But I have done 'going out' like that. I want to be around my daughter and not palming her off on others."*

*"With some, mainly career girlfriends, it is hard to make time as I am very tired in the evenings and at the weekend we have to fit around nap times."*

*"I have become closer to those with children and less close to those without as there is a lot less in common to talk about and they seem bored of the baby centred-ness of meeting up."*

*"Most of my older friends had children already or were having them almost at the same time as us. So we were joining the club."*

Making new friends or discovering a deeper connection to those who already have children is invaluable. We get to share the emotional load of being a mum and it helps us firm up our new identity as a mother. Meeting up with old friends can also be an essential part of reconnecting with ourselves as more than a mum. It can assist us in remembering ourselves as a person, beyond the all encompassing task of raising a child.

*"It helped having friends with babies who could relate to my worries and having friends who didn't have children to keep me normal."*

This early stage of motherhood is pretty intense. It is the beginning of a life with our child, one where we will constantly grow and learn. We begin to discover ourselves as a mother and start the ongoing process of finding our own path through motherhood. Now obviously, there are some huge issues that I have not mentioned as they deserve much more in-depth attention, which they get in the next chapters.

# Chapter Five
# LET'S GET PRACTICAL
# COPING WITH THE BIG ISSUES

So what were the big practical issues of motherhood that my mothers talked about? Well, feeding our babies is the first and possibly most controversial one. Hot on its heels was dealing with exhaustion as well as coping with crying and illness.

## Feeding Our Babies

All the research points to the fact that breast milk is much better for our babies in both the short and long-term. It also has health benefits for us as mums and helps increase the bond between mother and baby. To this end there has been a concerted effort from health professionals to convey its importance and so increase the proportion of women breastfeeding their babies. When I had my children the slogan was 'Breast is best' and it was used everywhere. This push towards breast-feeding has been successful. Statistics from The Infant Feeding Survey undertaken in the UK show improvements in the number of women starting to breastfeed and continuing to do so. But many of my women also spoke of the downsides. It made people talk in terms of breast versus bottle, as if it is an either/or debate with the breastfeeding mothers holding the moral high ground.

Before going out and interviewing my mothers I was unaware that I too had fallen into this mindset. I assumed this book would contain one section on women who breastfeed and one on those who bottle-feed. But this is not what I found when I talked to my mothers. Rather I saw women on a journey with their babies where what they did, with regards to feeding, and how they felt was an evolving process.

When we stop thinking in terms of one approach versus another and start thinking about feeding journeys, it all of a sudden becomes a much kinder way of operating. It removes us from the breast versus bottle debate into real life experience where we feed our babies based on the wider circumstances we find ourselves in, both practically and emotionally speaking.

As "The Guilt-Free Guide to Motherhood" we can't avoid getting into the emotive breast versus bottle discussion because it had a big impact on many of my mums. But first I want to start by looking at the feeding journeys of my mothers to demonstrate the variety and often evolving nature of my women's experiences.

## Feeding Journeys

Most of my mothers wanted to breastfeed, understanding that it was good for their babies. Abbey, for example, found that it only took a week for her to get used to feeding her son after which time it became easy and a pleasure to do, allowing her to breastfeed exclusively. Of course, feeding our babies is a learning curve for all of us and it takes varying amounts of time to become accustomed to it. Some of my mums, like Emily, did enjoy it but initially found it quite challenging.

*"People kept saying to me it gets easier, it gets easier and I just had to keep repeating it at the back of my head and actually it got a lot worse before it got easier. But when I came out the other side of that, (it wasn't until Charlie was two months old maybe even three months old) ....suddenly it is was easier and that's when I did actually start to enjoy it."*

For Emily and many of my mothers who were solely breastfeeding the sense of responsibility for their babies growth was intense and it could feel difficult when other babies were growing faster. However, once they could see their child gaining weight it, more often than not, turned into a sense of pleasure and satisfaction.

*"I guess the feeling of pride continued, 'Look at me, I'm feeding my baby' and watching the fat growing on his wrists and ankles and thinking 'I'm contributing to that', was a really nice feeling."*

Successfully feeding our babies can feel so natural but when there are difficulties it can become really fraught. Problems in feeding, no matter what form it takes, quickly becomes really intense and upsetting. Frances found it challenging to get her daughter, Paige, latched on, which became a huge stress, making that first week of her daughter's life feel like forever.

*"It was the one thing that made me very emotional."*

Breastfeeding creates a wonderful bond and connection between us and our babies and for more than one of my mothers this was healing. Frances, once Paige got the hang of it, found that breastfeeding her daughter helped her deal with her feelings of loss from not having had the natural birth she had hoped for.

*"I just found it really satisfying. Obviously you get that
lovely closeness of her being attached to you.
And obviously I felt a sense of achievement."*

These mothers got a sense of satisfaction and pleasure from feeding their babies themselves. However, not all of us enjoy breastfeeding. I talked to mothers who were not bothered by it and didn't have strong feelings either way, to those who actively didn't like it. For some, this was part of the journey, like Lily who really did not enjoy feeding her daughter to begin with.

*"I found it very hard coping with a new baby and the demands of
breastfeeding. I actually felt a bit redundant. All I did was provide
the milk and other people did the nappy changing and soothing.
I felt like if my husband went and bought a tin of formula then I
wouldn't be needed at all. I couldn't decide if that would be a good
thing or not. On the other hand, I felt trapped because Jess fed a lot,
so I couldn't go out without her even for an hour."*

Jess was a really good feeder but she fed so frequently that Lily felt imprisoned by her baby's need of her. On top of this, Lily found it diffi-cult because she couldn't know how much her daughter had consumed in any one feed leaving her confused when Jess cried, not knowing if she should be feeding her again. As a person, Lily liked to know what she was doing and in these early days of breastfeeding she didn't relish the uncertainty. Despite all of this, she decided to persevere. Jess put on weight, which gave Lily a great sense of achievement, helping her build confidence in herself as a mother.

> *"For the first five months or so Jess's good growth*
> *was all down to me breastfeeding."*

Lily discovered an unexpected pleasure in breastfeeding and only began reducing it when she knew she was going back to work.

Whereas, for some other mothers breastfeeding never became that pleasure. They did it because they could and felt it was what was best for their baby, like Eve, who was really surprised by how hard it was to breastfeed.

> *"I thought it was going to be the easiest thing in the world*
> *and it's absolutely so difficult."*

Her son initially was feeding every hour and then she got mastitis. Her health visitors kept on at her to continue although she wanted to stop. This pressure angered Eve.

> *"It is certainly not what you think it is going to be. It really isn't.*
> *But you feel guilty if you don't do it and the health visitors*
> *make you feel like you're feeding your baby poison*
> *[if you were to give them a bottle]."*

To her credit she managed three months.

Exclusive breastfeeding while being the aim of many of my mothers, didn't always work out. A number started with this intention, only to find that circumstances called for a change. Lucy and Liz both found themselves in this position. Liz always set herself really high standards throughout her life and she was no different with breastfeeding. She wanted to do it exclusively, for as long as possible. But after the first week she found that Spencer was still not happy so she decided to try topping up with formula. Making that decision had a really positive effect on Spencer yet Liz found herself feeling very guilty. She tried changing her diet but still could not get much milk. She tried expressing but after half an hour of pumping she would not even have one fluid ounce. One midwife said she shouldn't be giving him a bottle, while others were reassuring saying that she just had to do what was needed.

*"Oh but I beat myself up about that because I really just wanted to breastfeed. I was determined to be good at breastfeeding, but because I just couldn't seem to fill him up, I was heart broken."*

While continuing to mix both breast and bottle-feeding Liz was relieved after week four to find that the breastfeeding stopped hurting and became easier. Likewise, Lucy had a really good birth with her daughter but found afterwards that she did not produce much milk. She persisted with breastfeeding for as long as she could, expressing many times a day. Lucy felt pressured to continue by her health visitors. Despite being disappointed on stopping, she found that her daughter began to put on weight and sleep much better once she was on formula. As with Lucy and Liz, sometimes breastfeeding exclusively stops seeming so ideal when we see our babies struggling or hungry.

Medical issues too can complicate things. Being ill or having our babies in special care can make breastfeeding more difficult. This was the case for Drew who haemorrhaged after the birth of her son leaving her anaemic. Thomas then developed jaundice and was taken to special care. She expressed milk to send to him, only to get a comments like 'Is that all you got?' from nurses. This started Drew thinking that she was not producing enough milk, which really played on her already worried mind.

*"I found it a struggle until my baby was three months old. I found the responsibility really hard. When my baby was hungry I felt my milk was not good enough. I often felt like a failure."*

49

Once Drew was home with Thomas, she continued to breastfeed but she didn't ever experience the feeling that her breasts were really full.

*"I always felt that he was just sucking on nothing."*

Drew was afraid of formula, feeling like it was dangerous for her baby. To add to that, all of her family had breastfed and she wanted to be like them. Despite this, her midwife advised that she have a carton of ready-made formula in the house as a safety net in case her son got too hungry. Thomas fed very frequently and Drew's concerns increased about her son not getting enough. In the end her husband decided that one night-time formula feed would help all of them. After his first bottle-feed her son slept for much longer than he had ever done before and, with hindsight, Drew wished that she had not worried so much about using it.

The increased information out there is changing not only the amount of women who breastfeed but also how long we carry on for. This is a great trend overall but it was experienced by some of my mothers as a pressure to continue regardless.

*"The information you read and the messages from the NCT [National Childbirth Trust] and everything else just plays on your conscience. Every time I set myself a target and I think 'No I'm going to be giving up breastfeeding by this time' the target kind of comes and goes and I am still breastfeeding. It's totally a guilty conscience. Yes, guilty for wanting to give it up. Guilty because I feel like I am letting Charlie down in some way."*

The message that breast milk is the best way to feed our babies has translated in many peoples minds to breastfeeding is an intrinsic part of being a good mother. The pressure and consequent guilt for those women who don't, can't or choose not to was talked about by many of my mums, even those who did exclusively breastfeed. All (and I mean all) of my mums who couldn't do it or decided not to, at some point, felt guilty even though they were making choices that were in the best interests of their infants.

In fact, there are circumstances where breastfeeding is not even encouraged. Children needing to be in special care for a prolonged period of time are often bottle-fed so that the nurses can do the feeding when the mother is not there. A prime example of this was Hope's son who was sadly very ill after he was born and in need of an operation.

Sometimes breastfeeding just does not work out despite all the best efforts, like in the case of Mona who was probably the most determined out of all my mothers to breastfeed. Unfortunately, the birth was very difficult and resulted in her new son needing extra medical care. The nurses initially fed him formula from a cup, in an attempt to avoid nipple confusion, after which many attempts were made to get Ryan to latch on. A breastfeeding counsellor was called to see if she could get him to take to it but eventually the decision had to be made to give up and continue with formula. Despite the stress of that time, once it was decided on, Mona felt nothing but relief.

*"Who says breast is best? It's not always best. There are certain scenarios when you need something else."*

Mona expressed what milk she had but it quickly dried up. She was very disappointed that it did not work for them but wanted to focus on the positives that both her and her son were healthy.

Another scenario is that our bodies might not play ball, which was the case with my first child. I ended up in intensive care after the birth of my son. In the weeks afterwards my body wisely decided to focus on getting me better and just did not produce any milk.

How we feed our babies is not just about their health either. It is important that we as mothers are healthy too. Some of my women realised that they would need to stop breastfeeding for their own sake. A small number found themselves distressed by breastfeeding or tee-tering on the brink of Postnatal Depression. Helping to support a mother deal with her baby is the best decision and for some this meant giving up breastfeeding. Jessica is a perfect example. After a difficult birth she began sinking into Postnatal Depression. The difficulties she

51

was experiencing in breastfeeding Megan were making her feel even more distressed so she gave up with the support of her midwife.

At the end of the day, we have to decide what is best for us and our baby. This is not a simple argument of 'Breast is best' but one that needs to take in the wider circumstances and feelings that also impact our babies.

## The Breast Versus Bottle Debate

How we feed our babies has become such a hot topic that, as I have already said, often pitches bottle-feeding mothers against breastfeeding ones. Those who are breastfeeding hold the moral high ground and those who don't languish behind defending their position. By creating two clear cut sides, it fails to represent the reality for most women. This binary debate often loses sight of a crucial perspective about feeding our babies. What is important is that we feed our babies, full stop. The how of it is actually a woman's choice and there are so many factors involved that we can't apply generalisations about what is right or wrong to individual women.

I applaud breastfeeding and would love it to be possible for every baby but as I interviewed my mothers I couldn't help feel that it was a shame that so many felt guilt and the need to defend themselves for not breastfeeding. While it is ideal, some circumstances make it undesirable or even impossible. 'Breast is best' is a phrase that is correct in an abstract way. Breast milk *is* the best milk for our babies. However, it does not take into account the complexity of circumstances that we face as mothers. As we look at individual cases it is easy to see that there is not one absolute rule to suit every situation. None of my mothers took the issue of feeding their baby lightly and all made decisions that they felt were in their child's best interests. Women should, of course, feel proud for breastfeeding their babies. It is a great achievement and one that can be very satisfying. Every mother who breastfeeds can rightly be proud of herself. Nevertheless, those that can't do it or choose not to, don't deserve to feel guilty.

### Guilt Over Feeding Decisions

Guilt can have a purpose, it often tells us when something we have done is less than ideal. For example, if we said something hurtful to someone else, guilt can signal to us that we need to examine our behaviour and maybe consider apologising. However, many of us experience feelings of guilt from things that are beyond our control or where there isn't actually anything wrong, but rather we have made a choice in one direction rather than another. If you are feeling bad, normally over the decision (or necessity) to not breastfeed, then it is worth considering what your priorities are as a mother.

Sometimes exclusive breastfeeding is not the best option for you or for your baby. In some circumstances it doesn't work out for them and in others it isn't right for you. The latter of the two is probably harder to accept but it is important to remember that our children need us to be healthy too. A decision not to breastfeed or to stop breastfeeding is made for a reason. Some of us just can't do it, in which case it's out of our control. Like me you probably have twinges of feeling bad but there is nothing to be done. Some mums don't produce enough milk, some find it challenging to their mental health and some need to stop for themselves. None of my women were selfish or inconsiderate. They were just faced with difficult decisions and some found the balance of the scales fell towards not breastfeeding (or mixing breastfeeding and bottle-feeding), at some point in their journey. There is no absolute here and like giving birth, doing it naturally, while great, does not make one mother better than another.

## Exhaustion

I read loads of books prior to having my first child and came away from them confused as to why mothers talked of sleep deprivation. Newborns are supposed to sleep a good sixteen hours a day. I couldn't see what the problem was. My actual experience was that my first son did not sleep anywhere near that amount (he still doesn't require a a lot of sleep) and that the broken nights had me in tears many times. I am not saying that it was all bad. There were many nights when I relished the night-time feeds. I was awake feeding my son with no distractions, which allowed me to really savour the connection between us. However, exhaustion *is* something that we all experience as parents, at some point.

In the early days our baby needs to feed and be changed regularly. They live on a different timetable to us. They don't know night from day and when there is something they want, well, they want it and will let us know about it in no uncertain terms. As time goes on this changes. Time between feeds stretches out and we start to get more sleep. It may not happen according to the guidelines but it does happen. Until then, we have to cope with broken nights.

Before children, we have no idea how having our sleep repeatedly interrupted impacts us. Our body clocks are not set up for waking every few hours. Even mothers with 'good sleepers' can struggle. So for those who really have sleep-challenged babies, well, it shouldn't be a surprise that it becomes hard to cope with everyday life. Some of my mothers had babies who began to extend their sleeps early on with the parents getting sustained sleep after only a few months. Unfortunately, some babies are not like that and the longer the sleep disturbances go on the harder it is to cope.

**The Impact of Exhaustion**

Sleep is a basic human need and prolonged sleep deprivation has all sorts of effects on us. We can't do or cope with as much as we would otherwise. We make mistakes: leave cars unlocked, doors wide open, stair-gates unclipped and on and on. A few mothers described it like being detached from everything else except their child. We can at times feel tearful, distraught, desperate, resentful or angry on too little sleep.

Prolonged sleep deprivation has a huge knock on effect to how we feel about everything. We don't get as much done, it becomes harder to make decisions or to even hold a train of thought. All of this can then impact our self-confidence and we can begin to feel bad about ourselves.

Of course each baby is different but the reactions to exhaustion on my mothers part were very similar.

*"This has been very difficult. I can't seem to manage to do much in the day and this makes me feel guilty and useless. Always feeling tired really affects your state of mind and I am forgetful and unable to make decisions."*

*"Everything disintegrates including your confidence."*

Exhaustion is all encompassing. It gets its tentacles into every aspect of our lives, including our relationships. Our patience has all been used up on our babies and we are understandably less tolerant. When I say 'we' here, I mean any parent who is having their night's sleep disturbed. Arguments are more likely to happen when there are two tired parents and, in fact, they are also likely to happen when there is one tired person and the other isn't. There was a noticeable increase in the disputes between my mothers and their partners, which could be over anything.

*"I have found life very hard with such little and broken sleep. My patience is very short with my husband, though I can keep it with my son. We just stopped doing anything. [We were] going to bed early and just hoping."*

One theme that came up, not just with the mums I interviewed but also time and time again at the Parent and Baby groups I ran, was what I call 'sleep resentment'. The lack of sleep itself can become a big issue, with plenty (but not all) of couples arguing over the amount of sleep each other has had.

*"We sort of reached breaking point really. It was such a shock to our marriage as Oliver was such a bad sleeper. We were so sleep deprived. And resentment kicks in as to who's having the most sleep and all that stupidity."*

Exhaustion can emotionally push us to our limits, which can lead us to do or feel things that we otherwise would not think possible. A few mothers I spoke to admitted getting angry with their babies because they themselves were so tired.

*"She wanted feeding and I couldn't get undressed quick enough and I was just going 'Shut up, shut up' and that frightens me... I wasn't going to do anything to her."*

*"Early on there were a couple of times when I got angry because I was so tired and stressed out. That was really scary."*

*"Every time she cried, because I was so exhausted, I just wanted her to stop."*

It is worth saying here that recognising that our patience is running out is highly important. Being able to step away from our babies, leaving them in a safe place, is key to not snapping. Problems generally occur when someone doesn't recognise it and continues to feel that they have no choice but to deal with the situation. I discuss this topic in more depth below in the section on Crying and in Chapter Seven.

## Helping Ourselves with Sleep Deprivation

There are many approaches to dealing with the lack of sleep inherent in having children. This is some of the more succinct advice that my mothers gave when I asked them how they coped with exhaustion.

*"Some days by just plodding on at a slower pace and not expecting any more of myself than to feed my baby. Other days I have relied heavily on my mum."*

*"I sleep when I can. I let the house get messy and keep it to the basics e.g. clean bathroom and kitchen. I hardly do anything in the evenings socially as after the bed/bath routine, I'm off to bed!"*

*"The second time around I think I changed my mindset. I just thought there is nothing I can do. I'm just going to have to get up and get on with it and I did."*

*"We've slept in separate rooms a lot, to try and get more sleep, so that only one of us gets disturbed by Jess."*

Interestingly, more than one mum told me that the second time round they decided not to get hung up on counting the amount of sleep they had each night. Instead they would just accept that what they got was all that was available. For them (and me) this made a surprisingly large difference. It did not alter the amount of sleep but instead just changed their focus away from the lack and on to the job in hand.

For some of my mothers feeding through the night was completely down to them. This is never easy. If this is your situation, firstly acknowledge that it is tough and congratulate yourself for doing it. Be kind to yourself wherever possible. Do whatever you can to rest in other ways. Sleeping when the baby sleeps (or just laying down) and getting people to take over when possible, will improve the situation. Sleeping in a child's nap time may not work out but laying down with your eyes covered can make a big difference.

Whether you have help or not, seriously consider your choices. If you could be resting and you aren't, then question yourself as to why. Many of our behaviours come from rules we learnt early in our lives. For example, it may feel imperative to have a clean and tidy house despite being exhausted. Ask yourself 'What is the worst that can happen if I prioritise rest?' In this example, the housework will still be there and nothing will go wrong if it remains that way. When we are exhausted we work less efficiently, make more mistakes and get easily distracted. But after some downtime, we work quicker and more effectively. The other question that is useful to ask is 'What will happen if I don't prioritise rest?' Well, in our example, there might be a tidy house but there also may be a tearful and impatient mother later on.

If you do have willing help then there are some possibilities for easing the burden. Where babies are being bottle-fed, either with expressed milk or formula, couples can spread the workload. With partners working full-time we may still have to shoulder the majority of night-time care but a little help really goes a long way. The key is to discuss it and make a plan. I have heard of couples arguing in the night (with a crying baby in the background) about who will get up. This works for no one. None of us are reasonable at three in the morning.

My mums found it useful to either agree on a night by night basis as to who was doing what (before bedtime) or decide on a general plan. The majority of my mothers with willing partners made a general plan. Some of these are outlined below.

1) On Friday evening the working partner takes over right through to Saturday morning at eleven, so mum gets a complete night and lay in once in the week.

> *"Its just nice to know when you go to bed at night that under no circumstances will you have to get up at any time until you are ready to. It helps to get you through the week really, I think. If you are struggling a bit, it's the most amazing thing."*

2) Taking turns feeding the baby through the night.

3) The working partner does Friday and Saturday night but then gets a lay in for as long as needed to catch up on lost sleep the next day.

4) Going to bed as soon as your partner is home from work and getting him to do any feeds to midnight, then taking over.

Of course, there can be many other ways of fitting in a break depending on the family circumstances, if not at night, maybe in the day. Overall these arrangements made a big difference to my women. And it is not a one way thing. A father feeling competent and being able to care for his own baby brings with it satisfaction and a sense of confidence for him too.

My mothers also employed other tactics. Eye patches, blackout blinds, ear plugs and sleeping in separate rooms (where possible) were all used to improve their quality of sleep. Above all, it is important to remember that it does get easier with time.

# Crying

All babies cry, even happy and content ones. However, as we learn about them and what they need, we begin to get better at dealing with it. Normally there is a list of things that we can do when they erupt: feed them, cuddle them, entertain them, cool them down, warm them up or change their nappies. We learn that not every sound is a cry and not every cry is hunger. Sometimes it can feel like we just can't act quick enough. The milk is on its way and we are going as fast as we can but still they scream. Yet overall, when we can see to our child's needs, satisfy them and leave them contented, we begin to feel a confidence in ourselves as a mother and as an effective mother at that.

> *"I just enjoy every bit of her. Even when she cries I know there are only a few things that can be wrong and I can sort them out."*

There are times, however, when we can't stop our babies from crying. All the normal things don't work and we are unsure what is wrong. When this happens we feel an urgency, escalating to distress. Our in-built need to protect our little ones can easily turn into panic.

> *"Even now if I hear him crying and I can't do anything about it I get hysterical, more and more hysterical by the minute."*

It is very important to check out why your baby is crying if they can't be consoled by the normal actions. Are they ill? Are they in pain? Is there something that has scared them? Are they getting too hot or too cold?

It is also just as important to know that a baby crying non-stop pushes any mother to her limits, particularly when we are exhausted. It is imperative that our own frustration levels are on our radar. Anyone who starts to feel angry or fraught with their baby needs to hand them to someone else or put them somewhere safe and step away for a while. This can be a really difficult thing to do because we feel it is our job to comfort them. I remember with my first child I was utterly exhausted and he would not stop crying. I was desperate for him to settle but nothing seemed to make any difference. My frustration levels were going up and up and, although I felt awful about it, I realised that I needed to step away. I put my son in his cot, went round the corner, sat on the stairs and burst into tears. Surprisingly to me at the time, it only took a few moments for my sympathy to reassert itself and I was back cuddling him, feeling calmer myself.

I am not suggesting walking off on a regular basis, leaving babies to scream it out. But I am suggesting knowing our own limits and giving ourselves permission to step away when necessary. Babies need to be comforted and calmed but they don't need a mother who is losing her temper with them for something they can't control. Acknowledging the stress we are under does not make us bad mothers, in fact it is rather the opposite. It is actually when a mother feels she has no choice, no help and doesn't acknowledge her own building tension that she is most likely to snap and behave inappropriately.

## Unhappy Babies and Struggling Mums

There was such a range of experiences among my mothers with regards to crying. At one end of the spectrum I had women whose babies were easy to soothe. One mum explained that she had never had to cope with a bout of crying she couldn't quickly resolve until her son had his first set of vaccinations. He then cried for an hour and a half leaving her so panicked that she called her husband at work, not knowing what else to do. This was her first experience of an inconsolable baby after which he went back to being the content boy that he was.

At the other end of the spectrum were a few mums whose babies cried a lot and none of the usual soothers would work. This brings a completely different dimension to child rearing.

*"Oliver used to cry a lot in the first weeks and I found it very hard."*

*"I can't remember much detail about things once I arrived home, only that Elise seemed to cry all the time and sleep very little. One day she was awake for seventeen hours. I cried a lot too."*

We naturally have a desperate drive to stop our babies crying. Yet when we can't, it feels as intense as if we are in danger ourselves. If it carries on and on then it can be very hard to cope. A baby that cries regularly without us being able to console them can make it almost impossible to feel successful as a mother.

*"All these things made me feel inadequate and unable to cope. I just wanted to forget the whole thing and go back to work and do something I knew I was good at."*

Constant crying challenges us at so many levels both physically and emotionally. Crying babies and exhaustion come hand in hand and learning to enjoy motherhood is much tougher. There is no guide book on how to get through with a miserable baby. It is a case of using the resources that we have available, being kind to ourselves, walking away when the frustration builds up and getting as much help as possible.

My second son would cry for long bouts. All I could do was prepare myself for the onslaught. It certainly feels endless when we are in it but one key point to remember is that by being there for our babies and regulating our own emotions, we are doing a fantastic job.

Exploring why your baby is crying and what might help is extremely important. It may be colic that will pass or a problem going to sleep, but it could be something else. It is really tough to keep searching to find solutions when you are exhausted. Going to the doctors repeatedly is not particularly fun but necessary. It is useful to write down when your baby cries and for how long, taking someone with you who can support you.

There is information out there on the causes of crying with advice on how to cope with crying and colic. There are charities dedicated to helping families with crying/demanding babies. They supply useful information and much needed support. Specific details are at the back of this book.

Overall, what matters is that you are doing the best for you and your baby. Just because your child isn't happy doesn't mean you aren't doing a great job. With hindsight, I would say dealing with my son's crying was one of the hardest things I've done but it is also the thing I am most proud of. It felt awful at the time and I constantly questioned everything but I got through it and supported him through it.

## Coping with Illness

We would like to protect our babies from everything but sometimes we just can't. They will get ill from time to time and when they are it can be really hard to know what to do, especially for a new mother.

Each new illness provides a challenge. We are thrown into the unknown. What should we do? When should we act? When should we worry (although we are worried already)? A simple cold is not simple to a baby and it can turn a happy little bundle into a miserable crying being that can only be carried all day long. Mothers routinely talk about their babies being ill as the worst time they have experienced. Seeing a doctor or utilising local medical support gives us invaluable information and guidelines to know when to take action and what action to take.

Minor illnesses in our children need to be monitored carefully but it is often more about getting through as a parent. While there are no solutions as such (illnesses usually run their course), we need to maximise our own ability to cope by looking after ourselves as well as our babies. The longer an illness goes on the more important this becomes. Here are the top tips from my mothers on coping with an ill child.

*Make sure you eat and drink so that you have the energy you need.*

*If your nights are really disturbed it can be easier to sleep in the same room as your baby.*

*Where there is room, couples sleeping separately and taking turns will help maximise the sleep each person gets.*

*Foregoing sociability and going to bed as soon as your partner or family come over can maximise your time to catch up on sleep.*

All the sleep quality tips in the section on exhaustion apply here too. There are great guidelines on coping with an ill baby on the internet that run through the do's and don'ts of managing an ill child. Use a reputable site like the National Health Service here in the UK.

It is also tough when we are ill. Before being a parent, being unwell means that we slow down the pace of our activities or stop and rest, depending on the severity. However, our children do not make any allowances for the fact that we feel awful. They still need what they need and getting through is the name of the game. We need to be creative and rest at every opportunity, doing the absolute minimum required and accepting any help offered. Making every activity last as long as possible helps. What these are will depend on the age of your child. When I was ill I laid on the floor while my son played and slept whenever he did. Once he was older he would have the longest baths ever while I would sit in the corner of the bathroom feeling grateful just to be still. Another mum, who hurt her back, put her daughter in her cot and gradually posted toys through the bars while she laid on the floor.

In much of this chapter we have been looking at the challenges that motherhood brings: the tough times and difficult decisions. It can sound negative when we just look at what problems may arise but in truth life is not about positive and negative experiences, with the first being good and the second being bad. In general, the things we have to work hard to attain become the things we are most proud of and it is no different in motherhood. The challenges we face as mothers are not always easy but there is also a joy in finding our own way of solving the problems and discovering our competency as a mum.

# Chapter Six
# LET'S TALK EMOTIONS
# BECOMING A MOTHER

On becoming a mother our lives change practically in so many ways but emotionally too, it is a whole new world. We are now responsible for a helpless human being. How we feel and perceive ourselves, as well as what we prioritise, are all impacted. In this chapter we look in much more depth at the big emotional changes we face as mothers, so many of which are rarely spoken about in everyday life.

## Love

The truth is that the majority of my women were surprised by how challenging motherhood could be but they were also, if not more so, surprised by the intensity of love that they felt for their child.

*"A lot of what I have said has been very negative but I am so glad I have got her. You know ultimately it is amazing. It's just wonderful."*

*"Every little achievement my son makes, the cuddles he gives me and knowing I am the only person he wants sometimes, does actually make up for a lot of what has happened"*

*"It's the best thing that has happened to me. Even when you have your bad days, it is worth it."*

All of my mothers struggled to describe the love they felt. Women who had been talking so freely about the difficulties that motherhood brought with it, slowed down, thinking about how to verbalise the feelings they had for their children. Words just couldn't do it justice. With great love as with great pain, words fall so far short of the experience itself. Some mothers spoke of it like a love affair but then stopped. They knew it was much more than that; a different love to anything they had encountered before.

*"It's almost like a new love affair, in a way. I talk about her nearly all the time. Myself and my husband talk about her all the time. Thinking about her all the time. She is everything. She is just everything."*

*"I knew I would love the baby but I didn't think I would love someone that much. I love my husband but it is a different love... I love my husband and we do everything together but I would do anything for Violet."*

*"Painful. Almost painful, isn't it? Because you love them so much, you'd do anything for them. You would lie down in front of a lorry if you knew it would save them. And I know I would do it and I couldn't say that about anyone else."*

We know the love for our children is different than that for any other person. We love them and it isn't dependent on what they do or who they are.

*"It is completely unconditional and I am very much aware of that. I don't think it's quite [long pause], I don't think any other relationship I have is as unconditional as it is for Charlie, in fact, I know it is not. And it's, I don't know, it's a weird one because as I said before I don't know him and I've really realised that now, that I don't know him. So how can you love someone you don't know? It's a really weird thing."*

The phrase unconditional love is used a lot because it is so important in the parent child relationship. Yet still, when confronted with the intensity of feeling, it surprises us. No one could explain it to another person, in a way they could understand, if they have not experienced it. One mother described it as a secret society where only other parents can know how you feel. The intensity of this love is both wonderful (for all the obvious reasons) and challenging because it leads us to endure more than we would have thought possible, if that is what our children need.

*"You lose your freedom, you're knackered, you don't sleep,
the house is a mess, there is more laundry to do but
somehow this little creature makes it all worthwhile."*

*"The most overwhelming feeling was the love for this little
creature that keeps you up all night and screams,
but that you would ultimately lie down and die for."*

Just the sight of our babies fills us with this powerful emotion. I remember being blown away by how much pleasure I got (and still get) from just looking at my sons.

*"You can look at them all day long."*

*"When he comes to me for a cuddle, when he smiles at me,
it just melts my heart. Everything he does amazes me
and I often look at him and can't believe he is mine."*

We need love in our relationship with our children. It bonds us together. I think it is worth making a quick note here about love and pleasure. Mothers are often represented as the cornerstones of all care and love. However, all of us have times when our children don't fill us with pleasure. Indeed love and pleasure are not the same thing. We can love our children but not enjoy cooking dinner with them crying on our hip, when all we want to do is lay down and be left alone for a while.

## Our Priorities

With this profound love that we feel, our priorities in life significantly change. Someone is now more important than anything else and it gives us a different perspective on ourselves and our lives.

*"It's just that overwhelming feeling that someone else is the most
important thing in the world and you can't be as selfish anymore.
I don't feel like I have to compete with friends to go out,
clothes to wear, things to do. I've got my own
little life and I am very happy with it."*

67

More than one mother described it as a relief to be less self-centred. They could let go of concerns about their weight, clothes and house, because they had something more important to focus on. Another mother described it as a sense of detachment; she was so focused on her baby that everything else faded into the background. Indeed, many talked of feeling that they had a role in life that eclipsed all the other things they had done.

*"It's made me more complete, like I have a purpose in life."*

*"Being a good mother is more important than anything else I do."*

*"I feel I am doing something very worthwhile. In some ways it's increased my self-esteem, being so totally loved and depended on. In others, I've had times when I've felt very inadequate, although I do tend to get over these as each problem resolves itself."*

The word 'complete' was used by many of my mothers as a way to describe the alteration of feeling within themselves.

The fact that my mums' priorities changed with the birth of their child was universal, but how it changed was actually very varied. For example, some became less interested in their career wanting to focus on raising their child, whereas others found their ambition to succeed in their professional role took on a new meaning. No matter what we do with our feelings, our children become a huge part in our lives and so impact any and every decision we make.


## Responsibility

The love for our children comes hand in hand with the responsibility we have for them. The intensity of emotion that came with this responsibility was such a surprise for all of my mums. No one else in the world is our baby's mother. It is down to us to care for and raise our child. For most women (and fathers) this feeling begins in earnest when we have returned home from hospital (or in the case of a home birth, when everyone else leaves). And for many mothers it hits again, big time, when we are left alone with our babies. A tiny, fragile baby is in our hands, literally. Our relationship is just starting out; we don't know them yet and they don't know us; we have never been a mother before and there is no manual to say what we should do and when. We are in charge of another life. The feeling this new state of affairs provoked in my mothers was varied but it was almost universally referred to as frightening or overwhelming initially.

> *"The second night after I came home from hospital, my husband had to go to work in the evening. My parents came over to help me. They cooked me dinner but I was really struggling with breastfeeding. They left me at nine pm and I put baby in her moses basket and lay in my bed to try to sleep. I was very overwhelmed, at that moment. I was hit by the terrifying responsibility of this baby. I will never forget that feeling."*

There is an increased sense of vulnerability that comes with caring for a newborn. All of a sudden we have a little person that we love more than anything else and because of this the world can feel a much bigger and more frightening place.

> *"When they are first born, for me it is how vulnerable you feel in a big world. The world is suddenly an enormous place. It's full of danger."*

We realise that our lives are now fundamentally connected to our little person and their survival. One mother described her son as her Achilles heel, which is a deadly weakness in spite of overall strength that can potentially lead to our downfall, while another said this:

> *"One thing I often think is that if, God forbid, something ever happened to him then my life would be over, pure and simple. I wouldn't be able to go on living. That thought terrifies me."*

The thought of death is so painful that not one of the mothers that spoke about it could mention the word. They said 'if something happened' or 'if anything happened'. The word death in relation to our own children is too painful to even utter. We understand that even though we have only known this child for a short time, our lives would never be the same again if they died.

This can sound like daunting stuff but actually my mums adapted to it. Protection became a new way of being but it did not continue to overwhelm them in the same way as it did initially. The fear, while not going away, ran in the background and for most of us there becomes an active enjoyment in the dependancy.

*"It's lovely to be needed because you feel special as well. It's the best job. Again, it's scary... It can be scary and a little bit daunting. What if I don't do it right? But I think the thing you have to know is you are going to make mistakes."*

*"It's wonderful in one sense. And it is lovely when they put their arms up to you and they only want you and no one else will do. But in the other sense it is frightening isn't it? Because you are responsible for their happiness, their health, their well being."*

*"It felt almost like I was suffocating. It was awful to feel you've got this massive responsibility. But now I quite like the feeling that he is dependent on me. I like to think that I can be here for him really."*

In many ways the total responsibility of our child gives us a unique opportunity to act independently, which can be empowering; we are empowered to discover ourselves and our own capabilities through being responsible for our children.

## Worry and Anxiety

Motherhood opens us up to love and through it we feel deep empathy for our little ones. When they are hungry, sad or scared, we feel for them and it doesn't stop there; we begin to feel for others in new ways, particularly children. This was demonstrated by plenty of my mothers who were no longer able to tolerate hearing about other children in difficulties. Through being more open we can feel more vulnerable, worrying or even feeling more anxious (when I am talking of anxiety here I am referring to a severe state of unease).

> *"In a way I have become more frightened now. It is the responsibility of caring for and loving this being so much. And the idea of anything ever happening to them is unthinkable. I think that makes you feel more vulnerable in a sense".*

This quote from one of my mothers encapsulates so much of what I heard. This sense of responsibility naturally leads to us to experience increased concerns and for some, anxiety. We worry that we might not do the right thing, that we might drop them or hurt them, that they might be ill or that we won't know what to do when they need our help. This, of course, impacted my mothers to varying degrees. While all admitted having concerns at times, some women were affected more than others although a few were surprised by how little they worried.

A handful of my women, with more marked anxiety, found that it demonstrated itself in the form of images and thoughts of their babies being hurt.

> *"I just imagined me walking down the stairs with her and me dropping her and her cracking her head on the floor. Or when she was first born, that I would drop her down the toilet. There was a lot of that to start with but not so much now."*

> *"I worried that I would fall asleep and squash him and suffocate him. Or I would leave him and he would fall off and land on the floor and smash his head."*

Some of my mums had fears about their own strength. With a baby in our charge we suddenly feel very powerful. We are huge in comparison, we control everything for them: their health, well-being and safety.

> *"There is an element of 'My goodness, I could crush you'. You do feel very powerful. You definitely could do a lot of damage, which is very frightening."*

71

A couple of women spoke of thoughts coming into their minds of what they could do, accidentally or on purpose, to their babies. Some saw these thoughts as a test. What if I forgot this? What if I did that? What if I hurt my baby because I am certainly physically capable of doing it? How would I feel? Does the thought bring up the correct amount of horror in me to make sure I never do it?

*"I feel it is like I am testing myself. Imaging myself doing it and then testing what my reaction is."*

*"Suddenly thinking 'You're so perfect, what if I do something to hurt you? And then that thought and that image coming to mind. What if I didn't look after you properly and you rolled off the bed and hurt yourself or I didn't do the car seat properly and you came out? I think it is just checking yourself and questioning yourself the whole time. I think that is part of being a mum though. I don't just check once, I check twice."*

This is a tough topic to talk about and not something that is normally volunteered in casual conversation. But none of my mothers who bravely told me their thoughts, were talking of times when their babies were crying and they actually felt like harming them. They were speaking of thoughts that jumped into their minds throughout their normal day and horrified them. These were super vigilant caring women who completely loved their babies.

It is a good thing to get clear here that our thoughts and our actions are not one and the same. We can think something and act on it. We can think something else and not act on it. If we analysed our thoughts everyday we would notice many things that we think, some that we do and plenty we do not do. In fact, for many people, the more frightening something is the more likely they are to think of the consequences of that action. If someone all of a sudden was given control of a nuclear bomb then they would certainly imagine that moment of activating it even though the consequences are horrific. One mother described her thoughts as 'an enhanced sense of responsibility'.

*"I suppose you can sometimes think 'Oh what if I did that?' and then it just slips off though doesn't it? It just goes."*

Not all of my mothers experienced these thoughts. For the ones who did, most found they faded away as they adjusted to the responsibility. These women understood that they were only passing ideas or fears and even though they disliked them they were not a sign of a problem. There was only one mother within this group who found them more persistent and who took her thoughts seriously. This is discussed later in this chapter in the section on Perinatal Obsessive Compulsive Disorder.

Vulnerability and fear are part of motherhood. The overwhelming sense of it we experience at the start, does not remain that powerful. We adjust to it in some way. For all of my mothers the levels gradually subsided as they adapted to the responsibility and learnt to feel safe in their babies robustness. We find a different way of being and build a confidence in ourselves. As one mum put it...

*"One thing that I wish someone had said to me is that it is scary. That it is not always going to be brilliant and exciting. I think if someone had just said to me 'There might be times when you're really worried or frightened and that is normal and that is okay'."*

There is no timescale for this adjustment and we should not try to timetable ourselves into one either. So many factors contribute to how easy it is (or not) to adjust to the demands that a child places on us. Each of us will react differently depending on ourselves, our babies and our circumstances. We all feel worried or anxious at times; increased responsibility and new situations can all raise this very human emotion. However, if anxiety seems to be becoming a problem then refer to the section later in this chapter on Postnatal Mental Health Illness.

## Enjoyment

Some aspects of raising new human beings is wonderful, others fine

ne plain difficult. Thinking about this I wondered whether there
articular stages of their child's development that my mothers
hardest and conversely ones that were easiest. So I asked.

There was a general, but not universal, consensus that the very early days of a brand new baby and sleep deprivation are pretty tough. Other than that there was no point of our babies development that was commonly liked or disliked. We all seem to find different stages challenging and different stages easy (well easier).

Some loved having a dependent infant, others loved weaning, whereas some loved crawling. For as many that loved a particular developmental step there were those that just didn't. And even then it is not straight forward. Within a single conversation I would have a mother saying that the current stage is the most difficult because of the amount of carrying needed, for example, and then later on that same mother would also say that now is the best stage because her baby is really responding to her.

One mum became aware of this herself as she was talking and told me that the best stage is always the present and the worst stage is always the present. This has an element of truth to it for many of us. We are in tune with the joys and the challenges of the current time. The stuff in the past we have mastered (or at least got through) and the stuff to come, hasn't happened yet. It can sometimes feel that we long for our baby to grow out of the phase they are in, only to find that when they do change, we long for them to grow out of that too. At first we want them to stop waking so frequently for feeds; then we want them to stop waking in the night altogether; then we are desperate for them to sit up; then we really want to get onto weaning; then we want them to stop putting every single thing in their mouths and so on. But at other times and often in the same day as wishing a stage away, we long for time to standstill. We love them so much and can't imagine anything better than being with them in that moment.

The reality of what I heard talking to my mothers was that our babies keep us on our toes. They just keep changing, which is both a joy and a challenge. Each new phase brings something different. Each time they reach a new milestone, we have to adapt, be it moving, weaning, walking or potty training.

*"During each stage there is something else to be aware of and think about. As a toddler my son is into everything and can't be left. He is heavy and likes to be carried too."*

Of course, our babies vary massively in their personalities and this impacts on how things are for us. A mother with an easy baby who is relaxed and amenable might find crawling quite a shock because, instead of being able to get on with her chores, she now needs to always keep her eye on the little tornado. However, for a mother with a baby who has not been content, crawling may be a relief by creating another occupation for her child. Likewise, weaning was a joy for some whose babies loved food, while others had to contend with little ones who were completely disinterested in eating.

Our individual personalities and circumstances can also affect how we feel about each new development. Some women spoke of a predisposition to liking a young baby when they were tiny and completely dependent and there were others, like myself, who increasingly enjoyed their children as they became more responsive and capable. For some women having a lot of family support made the early days much more manageable, whereas for others coping alone made this time much more challenging.

Enjoying motherhood is not so much about the stage that our baby is in, it is more about how able we are to enjoy our children (hence the word enjoy-able). In the right conditions it is easier. Exhaustion, illness, Postnatal Depression, a crying baby, a lack of support and any other of life's stressors can all impact our ability to enjoy being a mum.

It is really important to understand that enjoyment and love are not one and the same. I didn't enjoy my second son crying for hours every evening but I certainly did love him. A lack of enjoyment sometimes is a part of life. While searching for ways to help their child, parents with ill or unhappy babies just have to walk the path until things improve.

Nevertheless, a continuing lack of enjoyment should not always be accepted. It can be a sign of just a truly difficult situation or it can be a signal that change is needed. Maybe your baby needs some form of help. Maybe more support is be required; sometimes an ear to listen to the frustrations of motherhood can make a difference. Or maybe loneliness or Postnatal Depression has become an issue, which needs to be addressed.

## Body Business

Unfortunately, we live in a culture with a very narrow definition of beauty. And although we know that, in reality, beauty is about much more than our physical form, most of us still find that part of how we feel about ourselves is tied up in how we feel about our bodies.

For many of us motherhood brings about a new era in terms of our physique. Being pregnant, giving birth and breastfeeding all have an impact on our body shape and most of these effects are the opposite to the image of the fashionable body, namely being slim and toned. Of course, these changes impacted my mothers in different ways. For some, the physical alterations were seen as a badge of achievement.

*"I have no physical effects or changes other than my wobbly belly and stretch marks. But I'd far rather have them and my son, than no son at all."*

*"I guess the biggest physical effect is my tummy. I have a lot of loose skin and lots of stretch marks but it doesn't really bother me. In a way, I am proud of it as I've had two lovely babies."*

Whereas for others the changes were harder to come to terms with.

*"I don't have so much confidence as my body has changed. I don't feel as physically attractive as I am tired. I think this does not help."*

76

*"I don't feel as sexy and I guess I do feel a bit 'mumsy' at times."*

*"On a more vain note, I was always very slim and I am really struggling to come to terms with being bigger."*

As one of the women above mentioned, tiredness really does not help. It is hard to feel good about ourselves when we are dogged by a lack of sleep or when there is no time to do other activities we enjoy. So many things change with motherhood and how we feel about our bodies is often a combination of the changes to us physically and how we are actually feeling. It can be easier to be dissatisfied with our waistline than with the loss of freedom that motherhood brings with it for a time.

Of course, on this topic there has to be some balance. On the one hand we don't want to value ourselves purely based on our bodies. People are attractive because of the whole package: the people they are, the energy they bring, their intelligence, insights and sense of humour. A particular body size or shape does not in itself make an attractive person. As mothers we are doing an amazing thing, something that is so much greater than ourselves, where concerns about body shape seem minor. On the other hand, doing things that help us feel nicer about ourselves and healthier is good too. Caring for a baby makes it easy for our needs to drop into last place. With time, my more experienced mothers found that seeing to their own general needs helped them feel better. By learning what to do to feel good about themselves alongside having a child, be it exercise, study or just wearing nice clothes, helped their overall feelings, both physically and emotionally.

## Postnatal Mental Health Illness

For some of my women motherhood was much further from what they expected than for most. Along with their baby, came a mix of challenging emotions above and beyond those that we have already explored.

Mental health illness is hard to recognise in ourselves at any time but at the onset of motherhood this is intensified because our lives have changed so much anyway. All of my mothers who experienced mental health issues after having their baby, except the most severe case, found it hard to identify in themselves because they believed how they felt was just about becoming a mother.

*"I thought this is life... no wonder people don't laugh when they are adults."*

We expect to get really tired, more emotional and even more anxious for a while. But Postnatal illness is more than the adjustment process that we all go through. It doesn't pass and it can feel as if we are stuck, unable to enjoy life or being ourselves.

**Postnatal Depression**

According to MIND, the mental health charity, ten to fifteen percent of mothers suffer from Postnatal Depression. It usually kicks in within one or two months of giving birth, although for some women it may have started in pregnancy.

Feeling low or down are normal feelings at certain points in our lives and motherhood is no different. So too is increased amounts of worry, which is common after having a baby. We are going through a big life change with many new responsibilities and challenges. With Postnatal Depression it is more than this. Symptoms vary from person-to-person but they include a depressed mood, feeling irritable or angry, being exhausted, problems sleeping (too little or too much), appetite changes, a lack of enjoyment in anything, loss of sex drive, negative thoughts, anxiety, avoiding people, hopelessness and maybe even thoughts of suicide. In my group, those who had moderate to severe depression mentioned how their personality had changed. Of course, the severity of symptoms vary; at the mild end of the scale it may be a feeling of being persistently low, whereas at the most severe end it may feel that life is no longer worth living.

**Postpartum Psychosis**

This disorder occurs in around one in a thousand mothers. Symptoms are severe and can include hearing voices, having unusual beliefs, being restless, experiencing confusion, manic behaviour, mood swings and delusions or hallucinations. It is absolutely essential to seek help immediately under these circumstances as it needs urgent treatment.

## Postnatal Obsessive Compulsive Disorder

This is a condition where women feel exceptionally anxious specifically about harm coming to their babies. It differs from the concerns that all mothers have, in not only their intensity but in the way that the women with Postnatal Obsessive Compulsive disorder deal with them. These feelings are overwhelming and cause the mum to spend a significant amount of time on behaviours designed to alleviate her fears, none of which helps reduce the anxiety. Time may be spent on excessive amounts of cleaning or checking her baby constantly for health problems while rarely being able to relax. It can start in pregnancy.

Mums with this condition may also fear that they will cause harm to their babies. As we have seen earlier in this chapter quite a few women have fleeting thoughts of this nature but understand them as simply that 'a thought'. With Postnatal OCD, this does not happen and the mother interprets the thought as a sign that she may act on it, which then leads her to go to exceptional lengths to avoid putting her baby in harms way.

Postnatal OCD is a much less well publicised condition than Postnatal Depression despite the fact that around two to four percent of new mothers experience it. The lack of information and the nature of the condition itself makes it really difficult for women to come forward and receive the help they need. It can feel very dangerous to go to a doctor and say that you have thoughts of harming your baby. But getting help and support is important to stop the problems multiplying. Postnatal OCD can be misdiagnosed partly because it is less well known but also because it can lead to Postnatal Depression as well.

## Post Traumatic Stress and Post Traumatic Stress Disorder

Post Traumatic Stress follows an acutely stressful situation. Anything that we experience that is life threatening or we perceive as incredibly dangerous is bound to have a big impact on us. Our bodies are cleverly designed to respond to danger and remember it, in order to keep us safe in the future. Physically and emotionally we react to the acute stress levels, which keep us on alert even after the event. This is a very prudent evolutionary tactic. If something dangerous occurs, collapsing straight afterwards may not be ideal in case there is more danger on its way. With time, as we gradually calm down we can begin to realise that the risk has passed; the levels of adrenaline in the body slowly subside and our ability to relax returns. At this point we are normally faced with a range of emotions brought up by the traumatic event such as loss, anger, anxiety and sadness. Trauma challenges our feelings of safety in the world and can make us question our life assumptions. However, as we process what has happened, we regain our balance. This is called Post Traumatic Stress and it is a healthy response to a threatening situation. It's not a mental health issue.

For some people this process gets stuck, which is where we begin to talk about Post Traumatic Stress Disorder (PTSD). Someone with PTSD may get flash backs or nightmares. They may attempt to avoid their feelings by distracting themselves, maybe even using substances to numb their feelings. They may limit their lives to avoid anything that reminds them of the trauma, feeling hyper-vigilant all the time, as if something dangerous could happen at any moment. There may also be symptoms like aches and pains, diarrhoea, irregular heartbeats, panic, headaches, anxiety, guilt, depression and sleep problems. According to the Royal College of Psychiatrists one in three people will find that their symptoms just carry on after a traumatic incident. They suggest that if it is less than six weeks since the traumatic event and you feel that you are improving gradually then it may be part of the normal pro-cess of adjustment. But if it is more than six weeks and you don't feel as if you are getting better, it is a good idea to talk to your doctor or a qualified therapist.

The women who I interviewed that experienced Post Traumatic Stress and those for whom it continued on to become Post Traumatic Stress Disorder had it because of either childbirth or a very stressful run up to having their baby. I reiterate that our body and mind react to how we feel about the situation, not the details of whether our life is actually in danger.

**When to Get Help with Mental Health issues**

There are no pre-defined parameters for seeking help because each person's experience of mental health issues is different. However, if you feel persistently troubled and things are not improving or you feel that your behaviour/personality has significantly changed, it is time to talk it over with someone.

Some of my mothers talked with their doctors and some to their health visitors. The range of help offered varied. A few women just needed some extra support and guidance in dealing with their babies. Some discovered that making a few life changes improved the situation, whereas others went on antidepressants and/or went to counselling or group therapy.

Most of my mothers found it tough speaking out initially. There are still remnants of the lack of understanding of mental health problems left over from the past. Psychological issues were wrongly spoken of as weakness, as if emotional pain is a personal failing. This belief is untrue. Although experiencing depression or anxiety tends to make us doubt ourselves, the truth is that no one experiencing mental health issues chooses to do so. So while it can be difficult, all of my mothers spoke of relief once they asked for help and started getting the support they needed. There are great information sources that cover mental health issues in more depth, which I reference at the end of this book.

## The Importance of Acknowledgement

Motherhood, as we can see from the above, creates so many emotions in us whether we go through what is considered the normal adjustment process or we end up finding it more challenging. No matter what it brings up, it is important to acknowledge our feelings. It is much easier to accept pleasure, love and the upsides of feeling responsible for another person than it is to accept any feelings that we categorize as negative. But all emotions are of value. As mothers we can easily stop ourselves from expressing the difficult feelings through a fear that acknowledging them means that we love our children less. Feelings of sadness or a sense of disappointment over our experiences of mother-hood are just as valid as any other emotion. They tell us something important, either about ourselves or our situation. Maybe we are sad because circumstances have made it hard to enjoy being a mum or dis-appointed because our expectations have not been met. This does not mean that we love our children any less. Acknowledging our so-called 'negative' emotions, when they arise, is of great benefit, allowing us to work through them so that they don't last.

# Chapter Seven
## THE LEARNING CURVE

Being a parent is a constant learning curve. As parents we need to find ways of operating and being, that work not just for our children but for us as well. What is appropriate for one family will not necessarily be right for another. Not only are our children different but we as mothers and fathers are different too and what works best takes into account the whole family unit.

The reality is that there is not one way to be a parent or one right answer. There are certainly things that we should not do. Our infants need love, support and care. As I have said before, anything that demeans or damages our children or ourselves is not okay. But apart from that, there are so many ways to go about raising a child. The unspoken rules from society around what mothers should do are rather restrictive. Yet, in talking with women from other countries and from different cultures, it is easy to see that there are a whole array of ways to be a successful mum that are not confined to what is considered the norm here in the west. Raising a child is a creative process like painting a picture. It doesn't follow a set pattern or any specific system. There are no formulas for what to do and when, that will give a specific result like $X+Y=Z$. $X+Y$ with one child will equal $Z$ but with another it will equal $T$ and for another child $X+Y$ is just not appropriate. We work with the raw material that we have, namely ourselves and our children. We take cues from our children and respond based on what seems right to us at the time. Much of it is trial and error and we frequently have to adjust, learn and change our plans.

All of us are parenting our children in our own way which is based around a unique relationship. It is great to learn and get guidance from others but essentially we are creating something new and original with each child, so there are no set answers or absolutes. The more we accept that there is not a formula or perfect solution, the easier it is for us. It allows us to embrace what we are as parents, rather than what we think we 'should' be. When we are freed up from attempting to meet everyone else's expectations, we can start to work with our children to determine our own direction. So with that in mind, let's look at the learning curve of motherhood as talked about by my women.

## Problem Solving

When things aren't going as we expected with our little ones, it is so easy to think that we must be doing something wrong and, in the search for answers, it can feel that there must be a right way to do it. From the outside other parents might make it all look easy, which can leave us feeling that they have the solutions and we don't. For example, a mum who struggles to get her child interested in food might see the mother of another little one who eats everything as doing better. But in all likelihood she just has a child who eats well and has never had to face those difficulties.

When we are searching for answers, it is worth bearing in mind that we are not searching for the right answer but just one that works for us. Sometimes there is a solution out there and we just need to find it, through trial and error. Sometimes though, problems with children are more about the stage of development they are in and something that we work through rather than solve.

## Taking Advice

As new mothers, getting support and other people's ideas is necessary because no one has all the answers. Books, doctors, health visitors, the internet, family and friends are all sources of information we can turn to. One of the challenges is that much of the advice is contradictory and this is because of one simple reason: no matter what anyone says, there is not a one-size-fits-all answer to raising children. Even professional guidance, which can seem to have added weight because it comes with the word 'expert' attached, has its limitations. Each approach (of which there are many) will have its own rationale but this doesn't mean that it will work, or indeed, that it is even suitable. Moreover, some of the professional guidance offered today will change with time. Scientific knowledge and our own understanding move on and plenty of what we believe to be 'right' at the moment will not be considered so in the future. Advice goes through fashions, so it is important that we take on board the information we are given but ensure we balance it with the messages we are getting from our little ones and our own senses. We are, after all, the one on the ground fully immersed in the situation.

All sources of information are just that, sources, and we need to pick and choose what seems most appropriate. When you need to solve a particular issue (or many) and you don't feel you know what to do, it is useful to take advice from a wide range of places. Hearing about just one approach can leave us with the idea that there is only one way. If that way works, then all is well and good, but if not then it can leave us feeling like we have failed or that there is something wrong.

It is easy to give the 'experts' more credit than our own judgements because they have a greater general knowledge than we do. My mothers and myself found some of their information helpful, but by no means all of it, as you can hear from the women below.

*"You don't necessarily take it as gospel."*

*"You need to pick the parts that you believe in and ignore the stuff you don't otherwise you wouldn't leave the house."*

If the advice you have received doesn't work for your baby or it doesn't seem right then there may just be another way.

## Dealing with Criticism

Unfortunately, as well as advice we also receive criticism from time to time. Sometimes it comes from unexpected quarters, from strangers pointing out that your little one should have shoes on (unaware that they keep removing them so have four pairs of socks on instead) to family and friends suggesting that you are not doing things quite right.

People can hold surprisingly inflexible ideas of what is the right approach and while they may have a valid opinion, there is rarely a black and white answer for every situation.

*"I am amazed at how many people start telling me what*
*I should be doing with my child."*

Criticisms can be tough to take, particularly when we are working so hard to be the best mother possible. We can be left feeling defensive, angry, uncertain and even in tears especially with our first child. On days when we are exhausted, a stray comment can feel like more than we can bear. However, as we grow in confidence it gets easier to brush off some of the things people say or we can decide to take the points on board but only if they are valid. At these times it is useful to have friends whom we can share some of the unfortunate and even ridiculous things people say.

## Making Comparisons

We are all naturally interested in other mothers. Through observing other women we can learn and get that invaluable understanding that we are not alone facing the challenges of motherhood.

Human nature dictates that we make comparisons. When we see others operating in the same way we do, it is reassuring and helps us confirm our actions. When we see people doing things in a manner we would not, then it can reassure us too. It helps us feel okay about the choices we make by comparison. However, there are times that we compare and in our minds we come up wanting. The women I interviewed spoke of this a lot. So many told me of feeling that they were letting down their little ones in some way because they could see another mother doing something different to them. It can be the smallest thing to someone else but discovering that another mother always cooks her baby's puree from scratch, when we don't, can leave us feeling guilty and questioning our choices. Or meeting a family who take their little ones to every class possible, provokes worries that we are not doing enough.

Making comparisons is fraught with problems. Firstly, none of us are the same. Our personalities, family dynamics and life situations all vary greatly and, as I have said before, what works for one child or family does not necessarily work for others.

Secondly, we can't really know what the internal world of someone else is. At a Parent and Baby group we might talk to a woman who has on make-up and is chatting away happily and think 'She must have it all sorted, why don't I?' But actually that mum has been stressed and is just happy to be out socialising, feeling normal for a change.

If you feel inadequate compared to other mums, writing a 'Should list' can be really helpful to release the pressure. Write down all the things you feel you 'should' be doing. Keep going until all those thoughts of what would make you a better mother or person are down on paper. I do mine as a spider diagram with the word SHOULD in the middle.

### *Example from my list : I should...*

*... cook more homemade food*

*... get fit*

*... loose weight*

*... read more to the kids*

*... keep on top of the housework*

*... have more couple time*

*... play more with the children*

Usually it is enough to make us see that, with an already packed day, actually doing it all is not humanly possible. The next step takes us a bit further. Cross out the word 'should' and write 'could'. Now consider each item without the demands of the word 'should' and consider if you could do it or even if you want to do it.

*... I could cook more homemade food but actually I do enough as it is.*
*... I could get fit and loose weight but I know that I am getting a little more exercise and I will be able to increase it soon.*

*... I could read more to the kids and actually I would like that. I might get them fed a little earlier so we can fit it in.*

*... I could do extra housework but then it would reduce the time I have with the children so I will carry on, even if it is not particularly tidy. And so on.*

Seeing our internal pressures written down in one place helps us get a better perspective on them and so take control once again.

Of course, it is good to assess our situation and consider the decisions we have made along the way. Learning from other women and having role models is a great thing. But comparing ourselves in a manner that diminishes how we feel about ourselves invalidates who we are as people. We are all just muddling through doing our best with what life gives us. If we learn something new and decide to change track then all the better. That is life and growth and the two go together.

It is the same with comparing babies and children. It can be very easy to notice what our little ones are not doing compared to those around them. But our children are as individual as we are. They have their own strengths and there are big variations in when and how children develop. Raising a child is not a competition. Books may have charts that give development plans but they are only a guide. One mother I met put it really well. She said that when our children are seven we will not be pointing out the early walkers 'Look at her, you can tell she walked before a year!' It may seem like a big deal at twelve months but later on it really won't. This applies to so many aspects of child rearing. The best we can do for our little ones is to take pleasure in their achievements and step away from feeling that they must perform.

*"You just need to know that it will happen. Just that babies are individual and you can talk to as many people as you can and you can get the great advice but take it with a pinch of salt. Don't compare your child to anyone because they will do it when they are ready to do it."*

The exception to this is when our children are a long way behind what is expected and so it may be prudent to seek advice.

## Guilt

When interviewing my mothers, without exception, I saw women who were trying their very best for their children. Despite this, the feeling that they were not doing quite well enough crept into many areas that we were discussing. As mothers it is inevitable and healthy for us to question ourselves. Am I doing it right? Is it good enough? Being responsible for another human being, with their ever-changing needs, takes a degree of flexibility. We all learn as we go along, taking on new ideas when appropriate. But it does seem that many of us are prone to feelings of guilt.

As mothers we know that what we do impacts how our children feel about themselves, which can lead us to consider the effect of every decision we make. Although there is not a perfect solution to anything, we can easily feel guilt about our choices. And herein lies one of the issues: that of choice. We have a lot of choice now. It sounds great because we associate it with freedom. However, when we have to make so many decisions on a daily basis we can begin to question all of them, as if there were a right one. What type of products we use, what we do or say, whether we work or don't work and what food we give our kids, are just a fraction of the choices we make. The funny thing is that the more choice we have, the less satisfied we are with our decisions. Even if it is the best one, we find ourselves wondering how we can really be sure.

Another aspect that can add to the feeling of guilt is how at odds the reality of motherhood feels compared to the social representation of what a mother 'should' be. The idea that mothers are these angelic, eternally patient, utterly devoted individuals who need nothing for themselves, still exists in our society. It is the perfect mother fantasy. But as we are real people with our own quirks and needs, we can find the reality so far removed from the myth that it can feel as if we are doing something wrong or, at the very least, not doing enough.

On top of that, motherhood is a hot topic with many opinions on the 'right way' to do it. There is so much advice out there. Not one person can jump through all the hoops and please all the experts, let alone families, partners, neighbours and passers-by. If we are looking for a 'right way' to be a mother then feeling guilt is inevitable because there just isn't one.

Now guilt is a normal human emotion that has its uses. It helps flag up for us behaviour that isn't ideal. For example, if I lost my temper and went a bit overboard in my criticism of another person (it has been known), then I would feel guilt afterwards. From that I would assess my behaviour and realise that, in the heat of the moment, I had said some less than useful things and apologise. Or, if I ate a whole cake meant for eight people (I am not admitting whether that has been known), then I will feel guilt as a way to tell me that actually it is not the healthiest behaviour.

The problem comes when guilt is experienced at times when we haven't actually got any control or made a mistake, so there is nothing to be learnt. Maybe we hear another mother talking about how she takes her baby out everyday and feel guilty because we don't. Or we read a book pronouncing the importance of keeping our baby in a structure and find ourselves feeling bad because that has never seemed to work out for us. It can be so easy to think that we are not doing well enough. However, much of what we do with our children is not about mistakes but about making choices. We simply can't do or be everything.

A good way to assess whether or not there is something to be learnt is to ask 'Have I made a mistake or have I just made a choice?' If it is a mistake then there will be something to learn or be actioned. If it is a choice then there won't be anything to be done, only an alternative choice that has its upsides and downsides too. It helps to recognise that we feel guilt because we constantly assess what is right for our children and so rather than beating ourselves up, we can congratulate ourselves for how much we consider our little ones and their needs.

It has to be said here that we will all make mistakes with our children and continue to do so simply because there is so much learning to be done throughout our parenting journey. It is particularly hard for us to forgive ourselves for the very fact that we love our children so much and want to make the best decisions possible for them. Nevertheless, all of us are fallible and so forgiving ourselves is an important part of being a mother.

## Coping with the Endless Work

Once we have children everything changes. We have the responsibility of another life, which brings with it a whole heap of work. We live in a strange twenty-four hour world of demands, where we work harder than ever but often find it challenging to say what we have actually done. Frustratingly, it can feel like we never complete anything. The housework, laundry and cooking are never completed because as soon as we finish, within hours, it needs to be done again. Likewise, parenting itself is never completed. In fact, with parenting there are very few specific goals that can be attained. Caring and nurturing our children is a constant, with no targets other than to do the best we can.

It is well known that humans don't operate that well with lots of tasks on the go. We don't get that much needed sense of satisfaction and achievement from completing something and our brain doesn't file away jobs that are part completed. Multiply each unfinished task by the hundreds of things that most of us are doing, add in the lack of sleep and it is easy to see how our poor old minds get pretty fogged up. Many of us feel a job is well done when it is completed and this can be a real issue once we become mothers, where nothing quite gets finished. The work in progress is everywhere, under our feet, at the bottom of the stairs, in our wash baskets and in our arms. That is how it is for every family. One thing that is guaranteed is that it will change. It starts slowly at first, but then one day we get to look back and see how life has altered, realising we do have time to get on top of things every now and then.

Before that happens though it is useful to consider the things that we feel we 'need' to do and really question these assumptions. Most of us struggle to maintain the standards we had before we have children, but being very careful about what we categorise as 'need to complete' tasks, helps us by removing the pressure to have things as they were before. For example, I had to learn that having the kitchen in a good enough state so that I could cook the next meal was a 'need to' task but having a tidy house was not because I could manage without it.

> *"I don't mind clutter, it is cleanliness... I would go round*
> *every week and I would polish the skirting boards*
> *and do the door handles. I was that finicky. And then*
> *he came along and I just couldn't cope. I was tired,*
> *I had him to look after, I had visitors all the time...*
> *I've just had to learn over time that my standards*
> *have had to drop a little bit but that took a while."*

It is also important to prioritise our own needs. They are as important as the chores and, funnily enough, when we have done something for ourselves we often have more energy for everything else we need to do. When we have babies and our day is spent just doing the urgent here and now tasks of feeding, changing and rocking, then the priority might be to rest in any spare moments. But with time that changes and other things can be undertaken. For me, when my son started sleeping more consistently through the night, I allotted ten minutes to write during his nap so that I could achieve something that I wanted.

If the feeling of being unproductive is particularly prominent then occasionally compiling a 'Have done' list can be useful. As you go through the day write down all the things you do, no matter how small: cooking, cleaning, carrying, cuddling, playing and so on. It is a bit of a pain but it's amazing in the evening to see how much is on there. I guarantee that any mother will use multiple sheets of paper. Don't forget to include the hundreds of out of hours jobs you do without complaining (well, mostly without complaining), the disturbed nights and the utter dedication that we all have for our kids. Any employer would be bowled over if we applied the dedication to a job that we do to our children.

## Coping with the Stress

Motherhood can be tough. There are no two ways about it. For all the joy that our children bring with them, there are times when we all feel pushed to our limits and it doesn't seem like we can take any more. Somedays there are just too many demands to cope with and we are just too tired for anything much to feel okay. There are moments when dealing with another bout of crying or a tantrum (depending on their age) is more than we can manage. Somedays, we are ill and all we want is to be left alone but the demands keep coming. Sometimes nothing we do seems to make a difference. In these times it is so easy to feel that we are just not good enough.

As I have said before, when we find our emotions running high, stepping away for a moment is important. Having a cry in another room doesn't mean we have failed, in fact it means the opposite, we are handling it by taking charge. Once we have released our emotions, we get back to feeling ourselves sooner than we could have imagined before. Of course, if you have a baby or toddler make sure they are in a safe place before you do this.

Understand that it is tough being a mum and you are truly not alone in finding it challenging. We all have our dark moments when we wonder what on earth has happened to our lives. What ever 'being kind to yourself' means to you, do it. Even the smallest of kindnesses can help.

When things are not going well it is so easy to start blaming ourselves. In these times watch out for that internal dialogue that whispers (or shouts) phrases like 'You are no good' or 'Everyone else does better than you'. It can feel like that occasionally. I know, I have been there. But if you wouldn't say it to a friend, don't accept it for yourself. The best reality check is to find other women in the same situation, particularly those who are willing to be honest. Hearing the difficulties that others are experiencing helps us truly understand that we are not alone. Even if we don't have honest mothers around us there are plenty of very open mother bloggers who share their own ups and downs. I have listed some of my favourite blogs at the end of the book. There are also some wonderful books out there with women giving personal accounts of the trials and tribulations of motherhood, many of which are incredibly funny and give us a great perspective on our own dilemmas.

Many problems that cause stress are of the time. Maybe it is tiredness (for us or our child), teething or an illness. However, if it's an issue that repeats itself over and over then we need to question it. Maybe more help is needed. Sometimes the challenges of motherhood are aided by some outside input, either advice or support. We are not meant to do it all alone. Or it could be that doing something differently will help. For example, one of my sons found dinner time very stressful. I was tired by then and so was he. This combination meant it was rarely a pleasant experience for either of us. So I began experimenting. I stopped meal times being about food and made it about fun. We sang songs, did rhymes and played little games, all which we interspersed with bits of food. It didn't take all the issues away but it certainly improved things.

## Building Confidence as a Mother

As we learn and face the challenges of motherhood we begin to develop a sense of confidence. We master those aspects of motherhood that we initially found daunting and we gradually feel more capable. We grow as people and parents. But even then, when something new is thrown into the mix, we can find ourselves feeling back to square one and unsure what to do. Children constantly alter and there are always new issues to deal with. But what gradually changes is our overall ability to deal with them. We learn to tolerate the uncertainty and trust that it will work out, even when we don't know how. Sometimes it is hard to see this growth in ourselves but it will be there.

## Valuing Ourselves

Babies don't directly thank us. They reward us (if they are well) with being content for periods of time but they don't give us marks out of ten for our ability to calm them down, or bonus points for hours of pacing the floor. Toddlers don't give us a pay cheque that says 'Well done, you worked hard', even though we are working harder than we ever have done. And it is not that we require this, we do it out of love. But a lack of recognition by society coupled with the challenge to meet our own needs while caring for a child, makes motherhood a strange place to be. This is where it is important for us to intermittently stop and value what we are actually doing as a mother. We are raising a child to be an adult; we are impacting someone profoundly. Navigating the complex path of meeting the needs of a family unit is not easy and we, as mothers, need to value ourselves and what we contribute, not just to our children and our families but to society also.

# Chapter Eight
# WE DON'T EXIST IN ISOLATION OUR RELATIONSHIPS

So far, we have been talking about us as mothers and the specific issues that being a mum brings with it. But, of course, we are not alone; we exist in a wider context with other family members. To varying degrees the key people in our lives all have a stake in our child and impact on us as mothers. Through our children our relationships with those around us change and in this chapter we look at what that impact was for my women.

## Parents and Siblings

Becoming a parent alters our understanding of our own parents. We begin to have an adult perspective on our childhood that was never there before. This deeper insight into what it means to raise a child, as well as the shared love that we have, often brings families closer together. For most of my mothers there was an improvement in their relationships with their family; their own parents became more involved and even brothers and sisters stepped in to support them.

*"Although we were already close, I think we've both become even closer to our parents. I certainly appreciate my parents and parents-in-law a lot more. Not only because of the wonderful support they've given us but also because I now understand what they went through to bring us up and how much love you feel for your child."*

*"I am very much closer to my sister now as she had a baby three months before me. This has been a life saver!"*

*"It also feels very reassuring when you see that someone else really cares for your baby."*

It can be quite surreal too, at times. Almost overnight the way we are treated by family members can change. As a mother we move into a position of being in charge. Our parents stop being the decision makers, as we are the ones who know our babies the best. We get to call the shots in a way that we never did before. Some of my mothers found that there was also a significant change in attitude from their siblings, particularly when they were the youngest.

However, for a few of my women, their family relationships were not improved. Instead of an increased closeness there was a disconnection because becoming a parent highlighted the lack of care that they had received growing up.

*"I understand my mother's behaviour less but paradoxically I have stopped struggling to find the mother-daughter relationship I craved."*

Most of my mothers felt that having a child had the biggest impact on their understanding and feelings for their own mother (and their mother-in-law too).

Motherhood crosses age, generations and often even cultures bringing us as women, if we allow it, closer together. No longer are we defined by our career, status or our background but by being a mother. It is a great leveller. There is a new understanding, even if it is only in a small way, of each other's experience and a recognition of the role that that person has played. With our own mothers in particular, we begin to understand their life experience with a depth that was impossible prior to having children.

*"In one way it is harder to be as close to your family as you're always busy, but on the other I do feel closer to my mum as now I know what she felt about me and how intense the love for your child is. I understand her and her decisions, about me as a child, more."*

Our connection to our mothers changes when we join them by becoming mums ourselves. Needless to say, women whose mothers had died or were absent, physically or emotionally, felt it keenly at this time. They felt the loss of the shared experience and understanding. But it went deeper than that. Being a mother made them feel connected to a person whom they could not connect to. For these women developing relationships with other women with children became very important.

## From a Couple to Parents

Having children changes so much: our daily lives, our sense of self, our bodies and unsurprisingly, the status quo of our relationship with our partner. Moving from two to three is a big adjustment for any couple, with the degree of change coming as a surprise for almost every woman I spoke to. We can feel at once closer together and further apart from our partners. The sense of being a family unit, can be wonderful. There is excitement and hope for the future. As a couple we fall in love with our new baby and share in the mutual sense of purpose. Seeing our partner care for this new little person is deeply reassuring and can make us feel even more love for them.

*"[It] makes me feel closer to him when I see him with Charlie."*

However, the exhaustion, lack of time and constant demands of a child take their toll, at least initially. All of my mothers spoke of either increased levels of conflict or unspoken resentments as they transitioned to being parents. The main areas that caused friction were related to sleep and the work-share but there were other themes that came up repeatedly too.

### Sleep and Work Share

When we are exhausted, sleep begins to dominate our minds and it is unsurprising that it seems to cause the most disputes. No couple where one or both of them are sleep deprived can carry on as before; arguments and disagreements are par for the course.

Obviously, each relationship is different and each family has differing circumstances. How quickly a baby sleeps, how much support there is, the health of everyone involved, as well as the financial situation all play a part in how smooth the early days are. But in general when we are tired, strained, have little time and our world is changing around us, it is very easy for frustrations to build up.

> *"The first couple of months were a nightmare. We were so tired.*
> *We argued all the time. It was a huge shock."*

Likewise, when we exist in a twenty-four hour world of demands then issues over how much each person is contributing become important, particularly if there is a large disparity. Nine of the women I interviewed (out of twenty-four) talked about resentment over them doing the majority of the childcare and chores, with eight of these saying that arguing became a problem.

> *"It has been much harder on my relationship than I could*
> *have imagined. At times, I have felt angry and*
> *resentful with him for not helping enough."*

> *"I knew that everything would be down to me and I just got*
> *on with it and was fine. It is now that I feel myself*
> *cracking at the seams a little."*

While I would say it was pretty common for there to be conflict over the workload, it was by no means universal. Six of my mums spoke of having very supportive partners who helped when they could. This does not mean that there was no friction at all on this topic because it was universally felt by each woman that they did the largest proportion of the tasks, both for their children and around the house.

> *"I think as a woman you always end up doing the*
> *lions share of the childcare whether you work or not.*
> *But he helps a lot. He does a lot of the washing*
> *and ironing. So he does his share, definitely."*

> *"I now accept that it is me who does the boring*
> *day-to-day baby jobs and no longer bear a grudge."*

## Understanding Each Others Differing Lives

With the advent of a baby, particularly where one person returns to work and one is at home, our lives become very different to each others and this in itself can cause difficulties. It means that we may no longer be in sync with the other person's needs. For example, being at home all day may mean that when our partners return we desperately want adult company, whereas they have been inundated with interactions at work and might want to be left alone.

It is also easy for there to be a lack of appreciation of the challenges in the other person's life. A few of my mothers said that their partners couldn't understand why, when they came home from work, the house could be in chaos and nothing else seemed to have been done. Without having cared for a baby single-handedly they are unlikely to know that an infant really can just take all day to look after. Likewise, the demands of a career and coming home to full-on family life is not always easy to adjust to.

*"When Mark comes home from work I have to make a conscious effort to consider what he must have been through in his working day and I hope that he is doing the same for me. Both of us have to work at that."*

## Changes to Sex Life

For some couples the inevitable difference in their sex lives caused problems, although it was not universal. Many couples found that both of them were too tired for sex initially but for others, particularly where one partner wanted more than the other, it was an issue. I go into this in more depth later in this chapter.

## Jealousy

Having a third family member inevitably changes the dynamic of any relationship. Being highly focused on our babies means that we are no longer able to be as we were towards our partners. For a few couples this caused a problem, with some of my mothers saying their husbands felt left out.

*"I think my husband felt sidelined."*

*"As a mum, it is very difficult to divide your time between husband and child. It is a big change for a man, not being number one all the time."*

## Wanting Everything Done Right

As mothers we really want things to be done in the best way possible for our little ones. If we are the one doing the majority of the care then it is natural for us to develop our own methods. Some of my mums then found it difficult to let their partner care for their baby because they would do things differently. A number felt compelled to takeover when they saw their partner doing something they themselves wouldn't do and for a few this stopped the offers of help being forthcoming.

## Different Approaches to Child Rearing

With the advent of children comes many new situations that we, as couples, have never been in before. This brings into focus the differing approaches to raising children that we all have. At some level, we will all base our parenting on how we have been brought up (even if it is to never be the same as our parents). Some of us see routines as essential, whereas others see them as limiting. Some of us are more physically protective than others. Someone who was left alone to cry as a baby may have trouble tolerating an infant that cries. We have different priorities and differing emotional reactions to situations.

*"Negotiating with my partner is tricky and it feels stressful as we have very different parenting styles in someways. I feel I am doing a good job but get no positive feedback about it from anyone except the baby. I feel frustrated that I can't do it the way that feels instinctive to me as a mother because my partner has very strong views."*

We all have our own thoughts and feelings about what family life should be. When we face these differences as a couple we realise that we have a lot to explore. I have to say though that for some couples these issues don't come up until later on, with the differing approach to parenting only becoming apparent in the toddler years.

## Being Parents and Partners

It takes time to work out how to operate as a couple once we have had children. In any new and complex situation we have to adjust and it is no different for couples raising a child. This is where communication is very important. Sharing our thoughts, perspectives and feelings adds to the understanding we have of the other person and together we tend to balance each other out, making better choices. With hindsight my husband's input has hugely benefited our children (while also being annoying at times).

It would be much too easy to say that these things just need a little communication because the reality is that parenting is about ongoing conversations between couples. As our children grow and change so do the situations they present. Likewise, as we learn, our understanding changes too.

There were three strategies in particular that my mothers found helped their relationship with their partner.

Firstly, plenty found that defining their responsibilities with their partners was advantageous. In the ever-changing world of raising a baby very little of it remains a constant but agreements on who is doing what at night and the division of chores really helped many of my mothers.

Secondly, (and this was challenging for some of my mums) was to allow their partners to learn their own methods of dealing with their baby.

*"What I've come to realise is that I have to let him do it in his own way... and sometimes I think 'You are doing that wrong' but it is not wrong to him, he has got to learn. I'm with her for twenty-four hours a day sometimes and he is only with her for a few hours so I can't expect him to catch up. It would be unfair."*

Respecting our partner's learning curve is good for everyone involved. It gives them time to build a bond with their own child and allows them to grow in confidence. Apart from something dangerous (like putting the baby in a bath that is too hot), plenty of things can be done differently and our baby will still be fine. Whoever is not caring for a child full-time, no matter the gender, will have to play catch up but that doesn't mean they can't be perfectly competent carers.

And this leads me onto the third strategy which is to ensure that both people in the relationship care for their baby for a significant period of time on their own. It creates a joint understanding when each person knows what it is like to look after a child unaided. This is not always possible, as with exclusive breastfeeding. But plenty of my mothers found it helped both them and their partners, who felt more connected and capable while understanding some of the challenges.

> *"All dads should have to do it one day by themselves*
> *within the first six weeks."*

When it comes to our relationship with our partner, it is important to remember that it won't always be smooth and that not all disagreements are bad. Sometimes they help clear the air and often, by understanding each other's viewpoint, we can make better choices. Having a child means that we get a new perspective on ourselves and our relationship. It is an opportunity to learn more about each other. Many of my women talked of their relationships becoming stronger, particularly those who had found it tough to start with. We become more flexible and adaptable, not just as individuals but as couples too.

> *"Now I would say we are closer than before Oliver*
> *but that has taken a lot of hard work."*

> *"It's brought us closer together but we have been really strict at being*
> *open and honest with each other. You need time for each other,*
> *with your baby and alone."*

## Sex Life

I asked my mums (who all had little ones aged between four months and twenty-three months) this question. "Has having children changed your sex life?" to which, without exception, there was some form of laughter. The arrival of an infant does significantly change our sex lives. Not one of my mums said she was having the same amount of intercourse and it is not surprising. There are so many life changes that come as a part of having a child.

There was a range of feelings about this change. Some spoke of missing that connection with their partners, whereas others felt that sex was just another pressure they could do without. There were couples that hadn't had sex for a long time and were okay with it, while for others it was an issue. Most were having sex but usually at a much reduced rate than before.

*"We will talk about it a lot, 'We really should have sex'.*
*'Yes we should!' "*

*"It is a bit of a bone of contention, to coin a phrase."*

*"It is really hard for me to ever explain to him just how exhausted*
*I am by the time it gets to eleven or twelve o'clock at night."*

The problem is that once we have children there are so many demands on us as couples. Men and women alike find themselves dealing with a lot more than ever before.

**Sleep Takes Priority**

Well my subtitle here says it all. If we need sleep, sex no longer feels as important. For as long as we are sleep deprived the bedroom becomes a place that we long for and only for the purpose of unconsciousness.

*"It is never the same once you have a kid.*
*Sleep becomes far more important."*

*"Sex life is minimal [laughing] because you are exhausted."*

*"The intention is there but the body is just not up for it."*

## Too Many Physical Demands

As mothers we often spend all day with our child attached to us in one form or another. We go from a life where physical contact is reserved for affection and love making, to one where we are more often than not connected to another little person. My mothers weren't complaining about that but they did find it tiring and many felt a deep need to be left alone at times when they would have engaged in sex in the past.

*"I just physically need nobody to be pawing
at me for a few minutes a day."*

*"It is like every one wants a bit of me."*

## From Mother to Lover

There is a big change in our role in life as a mother. Home life becomes about dealing with the permanent workload with no demarkation point, no line that says work is over and it is time to relax. Dealing with the ever present 'To do list' of being a mum (and dad) can feel more imminent than taking time as a couple to be together, making it tough to switch from being a parent to a lover.

## Feeling Different About Ourselves and Our Bodies

Sex is about so much more then the act itself or the love that we have for our partner; it is about how we feel about ourselves both physically and emotionally. When we feel attractive, happy and interesting it is easy to feel sexy and to want sex. Babies don't often lend themselves to this. A lack of sleep, no time to ourselves, sick on our shoulders and dribble everywhere doesn't work in favour of feeling sexy.

*"Some days I am definitely somebody's mother and I very much
feel like I have had two children and I am getting old."*

*"You just become a mum and it feels like you'll never
going to be a woman again."*

Most of us have experienced changes to our bodies during pregnancy and childbirth. For some of my mothers (certainly not all) weight gain, changes to their breasts and stretch marks all impacted their ability to feel attractive.

*"Our sex life is not as active mainly due to tiredness and a bad body image from weight gain."*

*"[I am] not liking my body much this time."*

A couple of mothers spoke of the challenge of breastfeeding and sex. Their breasts became a functional part of them and so lost their erotic association, which further complicated their sex lives.

## Physical Changes

For some women there were concerns about their ability to have sex due to stitching from childbirth, which delayed them wanting to try. While one of my mums actively had some issues with the way she had been stitched up, for others their reticence turned out to be unfounded.

## Resentments

Sex is about accepting our partner and being accepted for who we are. There is, however, nothing worse for a sex life than resentment. We don't want to have intimate contact with someone we are angry with. Where there are ongoing unresolved issues between couples their sex life normally suffers.

Beyond the issues that my mothers described, raising children brings a significant change to our intimate lives because it alters the way we relate to each other. As parents we work together to create stability while sharing the many demands of running a home and caring for children. We support each other and give of ourselves in so many ways. Unfortunately, as Esther Perel explains in her wonderful book *Mating in Captivity*, this depth of security which is so sought after in family life can be at odds with the excitement needed to fuel sexual desire.

With all of the above we can see that there are plenty of challenges to sex after children. However, with time we adapt, becoming more able to switch between mother and lover, finding new ways of being with our partner. Most likely it won't be the same as our pre-children years but that doesn't mean that we don't reach a better balance as our children grow up and we begin to get sleep and a bit more time to ourselves.

## Single Motherhood

Two of my mothers had separated from their partners and so had the added challenge of raising their child alone. With such a small sample, this can't be an in-depth exploration of single motherhood, but I wanted to mention the differing issues that this brought about for them.

Although it wasn't a situation that either had sought out, both spoke of how their lives would be harder within an unhappy relationship. Neither wanted to be with the men that they had conceived their child with and knew that to separate was the best decision for themselves and their child.

> *"Once you have children your morals and standards change.*
> *I won't let myself be treated the same way."*

Despite this knowledge, there was no escaping that the responsibilities of a baby falling on one person made it much harder work. The obvious difference was that the financial burden of earning a wage fell squarely on their shoulders, which made working a necessity. Although, in conversation, the most significant losses were less tangible. Those moments that we easily take for granted when we have a supportive partner, were actually really missed. Having no one to step in and help when things got too much, no one to converse with in the small hours about their worries and no one to just be there while they popped out, all added to the challenges. Indeed, both felt a real lack of being able to share their child's milestones with an invested partner. Loneliness was always a possibility, which made it all the more essential for these women to get out and create a support network around them.

Despite the challenges of raising a child alone, each of these mothers talked about the realisation of their own strength. They learnt that they were stronger than they had imagined through stepping away from a destructive relationship and coping single handedly.

*"I am still the same person but I have realised I can cope with so much more. I am stronger, happier and protective."*

# Chapter Nine
## "I HAVE NEEDS TOO"

Becoming a mother welcomes into our life so much that is new. A child, of course, love, opportunities for growth and a whole heap of work. All of this chases away much, if not all, of the time we have for ourselves. Initially, all of us put aside our needs and focus on the task of raising our baby; there is not really room for much else. A day spent caring for an infant, particularly if we are alone, consists of just that. It can be an achievement to have a shower and eat a meal. One of my mothers described it as being 'on hold' until her child got less dependent.

As time goes on, however, we all begin to need space for ourselves. For most of us early on, it is not major things that we desire but simple ones, like a bath in peace or having a complete conversation or going for a walk without a baby in tow. Many of my mothers spoke of just needing a break from always handling and thinking about their child. More often than not, in the early days, these are snatched moments when there are other adults to help or our babies are sleeping.

*"I made time for myself by having a shower in the morning to wake me up and by having a bath with expensive bubble bath at night. I closed the door and left my husband in charge and cleared my head."*

*"I still don't really have a lot of time for myself except in the evenings. When there are no jobs to do I watch television. When I get completely free time I might read a bit or sleep or look at e-mails."*

*"I don't get much time for myself, but if I do I try to exercise and I like reading."*

At some point though snatched moments are no longer enough. When this happens varies from person-to-person. I had mothers who left their babies for the first time at a few weeks old to those that waited until they were much older. Some admitted that they didn't ever get to the stage where they felt okay to leave their infant but they did it because their partners or family persuaded them of its value.

After we have bonded and cared for our babies twenty-four hours a day, seven days a week, leaving them is bound to be challenging. For all my mums the memory of the first time was etched in their minds.

*"I went to the cinema with a friend. I had my mobile on silent on my lap the whole time and I was very anxious. She was six months."*

*"I had to go to Tesco's and I rushed around getting as much as I could, feeling increasingly panicky and hating it."*

*"I left my baby with my husband in the first few weeks but at this time I was still breastfeeding. He was feeding every one to two hours and was always crying in-between, so I felt very anxious and actually had to return early to feed him."*

*"I was supposed to rest but believe me it had the opposite effect. I just stressed all the time about what he was doing."*

*"The very first time, I think was when my mother-in-law took her for a Thursday afternoon and Joseph and I went out for lunch. It was wonderful to spend time with Joseph but I did worry, not about Elise but about how my mother-in-law would cope with her crying."*

Worrying is completely normal when we leave our baby. It can feel like no one else can do the same job that we can (which is true). But with time we discover that other trusted people can do a good enough job while we get a break and come back refreshed or at least keen to be home again. There is always a pull to be with our children and for many of my mothers there was a sense of relief when they were reunited. But once we grow in confidence that our babies will be fine, we begin to find short stretches away more enjoyable and learn to appreciate the chance for the other parts of ourselves to breathe.

# The 'Me Time' Struggle

Within each of us are differing but essential parts of ourself. We all have our own desires: the things that fuel us and fulfil our sense of self. No matter how much we have enjoyed being a mother, at some point, we all begin to want room to express these.

As time goes on all the women I spoke to began to want more, beyond popping to the shops or the odd trip out. We begin to miss our own space, our hobbies and utilising our minds and bodies for different tasks than motherhood. The need for time on a more consistent basis gradually reasserts itself.

*"I mentally feel I need a break. I am at that point now where I just need to be doing something for myself."*

*"I could do with just a day to myself, not just a couple of hours but a day to myself."*

Many of us struggle with the idea of having time for ourselves, in whatever form that takes. We love our children so much that it feels like they should be everything to us and that our needs should no longer matter. Most of my mothers could accept the desire to go out alone for a short time, but found it more challenging to accept the increasing need for more in their lives.

*"Why isn't this enough? Why am I craving to do something else or to stimulate my mind in some way? Why isn't it enough to be spending everyday doing nothing but playing with my son?"*

This is where we really notice how pervasive the idea of the selfless mother is. Giving time to ourselves can seem like the antithesis of what it is to be a good mum. Being a good mother is traditionally defined by the ability to see to other people's needs. By its very nature it is a never ending task where more can always be done, be it housework, cooking, caring, playing and so on. With this can come a sense of fulfilment and purpose. As mothers we are aware of the power that we have in the home and the impact we have on our children's lives. We keep things

113

ticking over nicely by oiling the practical and emotional wheels of domestic life. The more we defer our needs, the more we get done and more successful we feel in our role. The problem is that with these end-less demands, our own needs can get lost.

Of course, if our child is distressed then nothing else does matter but as we see them develop and know that they can be happy without us, we all (at some point), feel the need to have other things in our life again. As much as the idea of being completely selfless and devoting ourselves entirely to our babies seems the ideal way to be a mother, to function well, we all require at least some of our own needs to be met. It is so easy to pick up the message that our role as mothers is purely about helping our children meet their needs. But actually if our sole focus is what is best for our offspring we miss a huge part out of the equation and that is ourselves. We could do every recommended thing for our babies and still not produce a good outcome if the end result is that we are unhappy. Children are brought up within a family and the overall health of that unit is crucial in their development, which includes us. It is important to recognise that what is good for us is significant too.

## The Balancing Act of Motherhood

Motherhood is essentially a constant balancing act. We have to balance our needs and everyone else's. For each woman and each family this will be different. For those of you without much external support then it really will be a case of thinking small and prioritising yourself whenever it is possible. For those of you with help, the options will be greater. Depending on their circumstances, my mothers found time for themselves to go to the gym, act, sing in a choir, watch television, read, write, go to the cinema or a restaurant, swim, horse ride, meet friends and surf the net while others returned to their old job or took on a new one.

*"I still enjoy it when I go [to the gym], though there is a pull to get it over with quickly to get back to Oliver as I feel guilty being away from him because of having to work during the week."*

*"One evening a week I go for choir practice, which is a real escape."*

*"I am lucky I have a family willing to help and they allow me to go to the gym once a week to chill out. My parents have my daughter overnight so I can get ready and go to work without getting up earlier and getting her to their's first."*

*"My husband has been very supportive and I joined a gym, went back to playing netball and [I] go riding occasionally."*

Sometimes starting small is the only way to go. Once we have children we can't go back to the range and amount of freedom that we used to have but we can identify what is important to us.

## The Career Conundrum

Part of considering our own needs both personally and practically brings up the question of whether and when we return to work. No matter what we decided before we have a baby, once all the emotions of being a mother are in the equation, it is necessary to reassess. Plenty of my mums thought they had a clear idea of what they would do, only to find that the reality of motherhood changed their decision.

### To work or not to work, that is the question, or is it?

As mothers we want to feel that what we are doing is right, particularly where our children are concerned. The question of what to do once maternity leave is over is often portrayed as creating two very distinct camps of women, namely those who work and those who stay-at-home. While there are people who have very strongly held beliefs about the right approach, most of us once we are parents, realise that it isn't a straightforward decision. Many working mothers acknowledge that they might like to be at home more often but also feel a benefit from working and likewise many stay-at-home mums would like the independence of working but choose to remain at home. Is there a right answer? No. The choice is for each family to make and it is a complex and emotive one.

The circumstances, needs and personalities within each family vary. What works for one doesn't work for another. This is not a one time decision either. What is right when our child is six months may not be right when they are three or five or ten.

The 'To work or not to work?' question needs to be put in perspective because, in fact, we all work whether we return full-time to a career, work part-time or stay-at-home. Some women go back to their profession when their babies are young, others when their child has started preschool or full-time education or even senior school. I have met many women who never officially worked but run a home, volunteer with charities and/or are carers for their own extended family. This is all work, just not the type with a financial reward at the end of each month.

The real question is not about whether to work or not but rather about how you feel about your current lifestyle. Are you happy? Is the balance good for you and your family?

Removing right or wrong from the equation and just considering what we (and our family needs) gives us the freedom to make choices that are best for us, taking into account the circumstances we find ourselves in practically, emotionally and financially.

Just within the group of mothers I interviewed the decisions they made varied widely. Abigail, for example, had to work to keep up the mortgage payments. She knew that the cost of childcare would wipe our most of her salary so she did three nights a week at her old job coming home in the morning to look after her daughter, catching up with the lost sleep whenever her daughter slept.

Whereas, Hope wanted to have a job but felt she could not leave her son due to his health problems. She also realised that the work she could get would not be financially viable.

Kayleigh was certain she would remain at home full-time, but when it came to it she felt that she had lost her anchor without her career so she returned part-time leaving her daughter in a nursery. But for Drew, returning to work made her feel very uncomfortable. As a couple, Drew and her husband worked out how to make the financial sacrifices necessary so she could stop working and remain at home.

*"I am loving it. Nothing is a rush. I have time for me, my husband and my son. I have lots of time to make motherhood enjoyable, meet new friends and enjoy these precious years."*

Eve's career was an essential part of her identity.

*"In some ways I need to work a bit to feel sane and to feel like I am something, [that] I am me, at the same time."*

Being at home full-time made her feel vulnerable and she disliked being reliant on her husband financially. Whereas, Mona didn't love her job and felt no loss for giving it up. Being a full-time mum made her feel happier than she ever had done before. For Emily, the decision to go back was based on a growing need for stimulating her mind and a desire to provide opportunities for her son later in life.

*"I do recognise a need in me to exercise my brain. And I am really surprised at how strongly I feel it."*

Her mother was available to take care of her son without which she said she would not have returned as early as she did. For Abbey it was the loneliness of full-time motherhood, especially with her husband away, that made her decide to go back.

*"I see it as my time for me, going out to work. It kept me sane. As hard as it was, it was also nice. I go to work to have a laugh. I'm a social person and I enjoy the job."*

Lily was anxious about leaving her daughter but knew that she would lose her position in a respectable large company if she didn't return to her post.

*"I think I would have chosen to stay at home if I could but now
I am glad I didn't because I am quite enjoying being back at work."*

She found that by going part-time she actually enjoyed the days with her daughter more.

Whereas, for Lucy returning to her career (which felt a pleasure initially) became something she disliked. It helped her realise that she was no longer interested in progressing up the career ladder, which spurred her on to look for ways to retrain so she could be with her daughter more.

Suffering from Postnatal Depression meant that motherhood was far from the experience that Beth had wanted and an essential part of her recovery was to return to work. It helped her feel better and reconnect with herself.

*"My day and a half in the office is important to me.
It gives me a break and makes me feel that I am
contributing financially to the household."*

But for Frances, running her business, keeping on top of the household chores and caring for her daughter left her exhausted.

*"Anything that isn't an urgent thing for my job or for Paige
kind of gets cut out of the equation."*

Frances was aware that the balance wasn't right for her and that something needed to change but she wasn't sure how, as she did not want to be a full-time mother.

Both Amanda and Naomi decided to be stay-at-home mums with Amanda knowing from the start that she didn't want to return to work until her children were in full-time education. Naomi went back initially but stopped after becoming increasingly unhappy with her son's childcare. Despite feeling guilt over no longer bringing in an income, she was pleased with her decision.

*"I don't want to work. I am not being lazy.*
*It is twenty-four hours [motherhood]. I really enjoy it.*
*I'd rather do this job than go and work for someone else."*

All of these women have made choices based on their circumstances and how they felt. It is hardly fair to compare them or see one group as better than the other. In fact, I didn't see distinct groups of mothers, delineated by working or not working; rather I saw women making decisions on what is best for their families. What I was struck by was not the right and wrong of working versus staying at home, but rather how amazing we are at adapting to what is needed. As women we can be very creative in our ability to adjust to the demands of family life, finding spaces to meet both our family's and our own needs.

My mothers followed similar patterns to our national trends with 70% returning to work. The more important statistic in my mind was that 20% of my mums were unhappy about their current situation. Either they wanted to work but couldn't or they were working but wanted to be with their child more. In my mind the question is not about working or not working but about how we feel about our work/family balance.

## What my Mums Said

So if you are in the throes of making a decision about what is right for you and your family then you might find it useful to know what my mothers said about their choices. I have compiled lists below making it easy to see how diverse and even opposite the opinions are depending on the individual. You may find statements that ring true for you and many that don't. There has been more said about working than staying at home simply because more of my mothers returned to work than didn't. But I also have to point out that when talking about work, the majority are referring to part-time hours.

## What WORKING Mums Said

*We have a better standard of living because we both work.*
*Financially contributing to the household feels good.*
*I wanted to return initially but now I would rather be at home.*

*I would not work if money was not an issue.*

*It's too hard to be a full-time mum.*

*I feel too vulnerable to be a stay-at-home mum.*

*It's so hard to leave my child but continuing work in the long-term is a good thing, if tough in the short-term.*

*I feel panicked about keeping up with the housework.*

*There is no time for myself, as work and my child are the priorities.*

*I want to be a good role model by working and being successful.*

*I have more drive to achieve in my career.*

*I have less drive to achieve at work as the kids are my priority now.*

*I had nothing to talk about when I was at home.*

*Work keeps me sane.*

*Work helps me cope with Postnatal Depression.*

*Work gives me confidence that I lose at home.*

*I feel myself, not just 'Mummy'.*

*Work helps me with my identity and what to say for myself.*

*My marriage is better as I feel better about myself.*

*I enjoy time with my child more now I am at work.*

*Work is a recharge for me and so I am a better mum.*

*Work offers me a break.*

Whether they felt happy to return to work or were doing it through necessity, every mother I spoke to said it was really hard to leave their child in the hands of someone else. The only mothers who this didn't apply to were those who did night work and left their babies at home with family to sleep. Even for those leaving their little ones with their own parents, stepping away from the connection was a wrench initially.

Childcare is a big issue. Being happy with the care of our children is essential not only for them but for us too. We all have moments of doubt when leaving them in the hands of other people and it can be agony to walk away when they are crying for us. It is important that children have secure relationships and that they have people they can turn to when they need help and support. Once we can see that they are coping and then even flourishing, as plenty of my mothers mentioned, we begin to relax.

Another of the challenges of returning to work is fitting everything in. The demands of home life do not disappear and the extra pull on our time can create more pressure. Under these circumstances it is worth considering what things you can do in order to make your life easier. However, for plenty of my mums the opposite was true. The hours of working gave them a break. Being energised and stimulated made it easier to feel on top of all the tasks at home.

## What Stay-at-Home Mums Said

*I see raising my children as a chapter in my life that I don't want to miss out on.*

*I really want to be able to drop my kids off at school and be able to pick them up.*

*I want to be the one caring for my children.*

*I don't want to have my baby in childcare.*

*I want to enjoy time with my child and not feel pressured by work.*

*I was so unhappy when I went back to my job.*

*I didn't expect to want to be a full-time mum.*

*I miss dressing up and going out.*

*I miss the social aspect of work.*

*It can feel isolating as most friends have gone back to their career.*

*I feel the need to justify my time as I am not earning.*

*I feel pressure to earn but I am unsure why as I work very hard at home.*

*I feel guilt at spending money I don't earn.*

*It is scary not knowing what the future will hold work wise now I've given up my job.*

*I am happy with my choice but I feel deskilled.*

Being a stay-at-home mum is not the easy option that it can appear on the surface. We get to define our days and be with our children; we have a level of freedom that working mothers don't, giving us time to explore and experiment, but it comes at a price. The home is our work place and we never get away from it. It can be hard to connect with a sense of achievement when the tasks resemble a treadmill; they just keep coming round and round and there is no pay cheque at the end of the month to reward us. If our partners and family work then it is easy to start feeling lonely and isolated. Days roll into one another quite easily. We can forget what day of the month it is or even which day of the week. Stay-at-home mums need to create a life that works for themselves as well as their children.

## A Note about Guilt

With this topic, guilt is generally linked to working mothers, probably because traditionally women stayed at home. But in reality both full-time mums and working mums felt guilt, at times, over their choice. When we go out to work the guilt often centres around not being with our children and being less available when we are home because we have other things to do. Whereas, for stay-at-home mums the guilt mostly centres around not bringing in an income, creating (in some) the feeling that they have to work extra hard to justify this. Many of my stay-at-home mothers said they noticed they were in the minority and felt a pressure to work. In *The Mommy Myth*, Susan J Douglas sums up the social dilemma women find themselves in really well, explaining how our culture makes full-time mothers seem boring and working mothers neglectful. In other words, we can't win.

Nevertheless, when we realise this, it can help us to stop comparing. Regardless of the social demands, we need to do what is best for ourselves and our family. There is no perfect solution either. At times being a stay-at-home mum will feel wonderful and at others it will feel too much or too confining. Likewise, being a working mum can feel like a liberation and at others moments it will feel impossibly tough to juggle both a child and the demands of a job.

# Chapter Ten
# LEARNING & LOOKING
# TO THE FUTURE

Motherhood is a process. It is a journey. Some of it will be amazing, some of it will be awful and a lot of it will just be. There is an ebb and flow to it. In any one day we can be loving it, hating it, getting on with it and just too busy to be feeling anything much at all about it. The one certain thing is that we will learn. We will learn about children, we will learn about life and most of all we will learn about ourselves.

## Unconditional Love

Through the love we have for our children our perspective changes forever. We get to love another person with no limits. No matter what they do, we love them. In this, there is great growth and great healing. Through loving our children we encounter our own strength in a way that we have never done before, experiencing ourselves differently, which ultimately helps us learn about ourselves.

## Just Being

Being a parent makes us experience the world around us in another way. One of the paradoxes of having children is that, on the one hand, they bring with them a lot of work but, on the other, they also make us slow down and appreciate the smaller details of life. As adults we often stop really seeing the world or appreciating the present moment, because it seems like we know about it all already. We get caught up in planning for the future or thinking of what has passed. However, through our children we begin to see more. At first babies notice just us, they stare intently at our faces and we notice them in all their uniqueness. Being with a baby is about just 'being'. They don't care about how we look or if there are cobwebs in the corner. They, and so to a certain extent we, begin to exist in the moment. As they mature they go on to be interested in everything. Through their discovery of the world we begin to see things through their eyes. For moments in time we are transported away from the 'Seen it all before' and 'I'm busy right now' mindset and back into that open and curious place that children inhabit. We are introduced once again to the concept of just being.

> *"I'm still the same person. If anything I am a better person who appreciates the simple things in life."*

## Childhood from a Different Perspective

Another perspective change is that we get to understand childhood as an adult. We experience being young again from the other side of the coin – being a parent. For many of us it is a subtle but still profound sensation where we begin to understand ourselves from another vantage point; one where we see our history, our parenting and ourselves in the world, differently. For me, watching my children's journey through life has helped me understand my own. It helped me realise how tough it is at times to be a child, allowing me to view myself much more kindly then I ever did before.

## Learning About Ourselves

As part of the interviews I conducted I asked my mothers what they had learnt about themselves since becoming a parent and the replies were plentiful and varied.

Motherhood, as we have heard, pushes us into situations we have never had to deal with before. Regardless of how we feel, we cope. We have ultimate responsibility for our children and for many women this has helped them discover their own strength and determination.

> *"[I have learnt] how much I can give and how much stamina I have."*

*"I have learnt that I am a coper and I am sometimes
amazed at how much I can juggle at once."*

*"I've learnt that I really have the ability to push the
boat out on a long-term basis."*

Having another person so reliant on them made many of my mums value themselves in a way that they had not done before. Knowing we are important and needed can push us to be the best version of ourselves.

*"I guess I have become a stronger person who won't let people
walk all over me like I did before. I'm a lot more confident."*

*"I have much more determination than I thought."*

*"[I have learnt] that I can be quite strong and
that I shouldn't be afraid of anyone."*

*"[I have learnt] that I can embrace new experiences and get
myself out there, despite not knowing what to expect."*

*"Since becoming a mother I've handled situations much better.
I think it is because I have someone else to consider and
I don't want her growing up with the same fears."*

A number of women spoke of discovering a level of patience within them that they did not know existed, while others talked of growing up and feeling less self-centred. The learning we gain with our children is endless.

Some of my mothers found themselves feeling less capable than ever before. They had to face their fragility. Others found that they were uncomfortable without a career to define them. While some discovered that they were a lot less patient than expected, with a few coming up against self-esteem issues or a need for control.

*"It's highlighted things I already knew, such as a tendency to feel
I am not good enough at things and not being comfortable
with a lack of structure, control etc. I have got much better at
going with the flow and taking each day as it comes."*

*"I find it incredible that a person that copes so well and
has a very responsible job can fall to pieces so easily."*

*"My whole identity was work. I really had no idea about me before I
had my daughter. I was really good at listening to others [as at work]
but found it really hard when people wanted to know about me."*

*"I would go round every week and I would polish the skirting
boards and do the door handles. I was that finicky.
And then he came along and I just couldn't cope."*

*"[I learnt] that I wasn't super woman and I can't do everything."*

*"I've got very high expectations of myself. I always have done.
I've always set my self really high goals... I've realised
I can still aim high but I have to do it in tiny little steps."*

We can see ourselves as having failed when we find something more challenging than we were expecting. But, more often than not, the greatest learning we have in life is through not succeeding, not being as we expected or what we expected. We learn about ourselves, about life and people in general. As a consequence we learn to be gentler and more flexible individuals.

As a society we tend to categorise experiences as positive or negative. If I discover that I am stronger than I thought, then that is a positive experience, whereas if I find that I am less patient than I thought, then that is a negative experience. But all learning is of value. In life, the more we understand about ourselves, the more we can successfully navigate the path ahead. Being faced with our own shortcomings gives us a chance to learn about ourselves in a way we can't when everything is going according to plan. We can use that knowledge to make better decisions in the future about what will or will not work for us. On a deeper level, we can use that information to discover more about ourselves by examining the feelings and considering where they might have come from. So if we find we are less patient than we expected it is a chance to consider what is triggering it and why that might be. If we find that we feel lost without having a job then we can begin to reflect on our identity as a person and explore who we are in a less defined role.

We learn a lot through challenges. When we are pushed and have few options we have to pull out of ourselves resources that we otherwise wouldn't have to find and there is no better incentive than our children. They make us want to be better people. The women I interviewed all found that they had grown through the challenges of motherhood, becoming more than they thought they could be, finding greater strengths than they knew.

The other thing that motherhood taught many of my mothers, myself included, was flexibility. Through raising a child we can become less judgemental because we learn about how complex life is.

*"Before I had children I criticised everybody else. I definitely thought I knew how to parent. Whereas now, I'm less critical of people because I can see that I might be the woman in Tesco's that is screaming at her children"*

*"I think I've become a little more open minded to other people's choices."*

## Looking to the Future

Initially with an infant in our charge it can be hard to see anything except what we are doing. We get fully absorbed into motherhood. At some point though we start to look beyond the present moment. As we get used to being a mother, with all it entails, we can raise our heads to think, once again, of our future and consider what it might look like.

**More Children**

When we look to the future one of the big considerations is about whether we try for another child. Plenty of my mums, particularly those with the youngest babies found it hard to imagine having another, either because it was too much work in the present moment or because they simply could not imagine loving another child in the same way. However, for some it was a given as they had always wanted two, three or even four kids. While for others the desire for more children came about through their enjoyment of motherhood. Plenty of my mums liked the idea of having a sibling as much for their existing child as for themselves.

Having already made the life alterations necessary to accommodate a baby most of my mothers knew they would be taking on more work but they also knew that they had learnt and developed so much. Most felt an increased belief in themselves to manage and be resourceful. Although a number mentioned that childbirth was a greater concern the second time round.

On the other hand, there were those women who did not want any more children. They were either satisfied with the number they had or they felt that they would not want to go through the whole process again. The decision to have no more children can bring with it a mixture of feelings. As our child moves through each stage of development it can feel liberating but, at the same time, it can also be a loss because we know we will never have a child at that stage again. There is, of course, no right choice over having more children, only a personal decision.

**Beyond Children**

Mothering offers us so much. The inevitable learning curve empowers us for the future. The skills we learn through being a mum can be brought to everything else we do. The knowledge we have gained about ourselves will naturally be utilised in whatever path we choose to walk.

However, in the short to mid-term, when we look to the future we can see that motherhood also limits us. We have less time, more work and commitments to juggle. The future can look more complex simply because it is. These limitations can be disheartening. We can't go back to the way we used to work or socialise. The arrangements surrounding any activities in our lives get much more involved. We need childcare, babysitters and backup plans for when our children are ill. While, on the one hand, I can see that our society isn't particularly family friendly, certainly when it comes to working, I have also been impressed by the creativity these limitations have shown in my mothers. Being restricted can feel frustrating but through it we are pushed to use our ingenuity and be resourceful. Time and time again I have seen women who have more demands on them and more to juggle but who find their own unique approaches to their lives.

Through motherhood plenty of us embark on a previously unconsidered path in life. I have met women who have returned to their old jobs but also those who have taken new career paths, started their own business, re-trained and those who have used it to break from the mould they were in and reach for their dreams.

## Motherhood

We can't know what it is to be a mother before we get there. Before I had children my answer to the question 'How will my life change?' fell so far short of the truth that it is truly laughable now. But that is how life is, we can't know an experience until we have had it and motherhood is just one of those journeys which nothing can really prepare us for.

*"I don't think there is anything anyone could have told me that I would have understood fully until I had a child.*
*Your world changes and that is about all you can guarantee".*

*"It has all been a learning experience and I don't think you can know more in advance".*

Motherhood can't be planned for because it impacts us in so many ways that are impossible to know in advance. We just immerse ourselves in it, finding our own path as we go along. And even then it just keeps changing. As a mother of primary school age children I'm still learning and developing. There are things that I do now that I would have never imagined years back and there are even some that I would have disagreed with when I started out.

Motherhood is not a job and it is not even a role, in the sense that we can step in and out of it when we want. It becomes a part of us. We love wholeheartedly and give of ourselves. In doing so we get back so much, learning about the people we are and life in general. Being a mother is creativity in action. We work with the unique combination of ourselves, our children and our circumstances. Dealing with the contradictions and challenges of motherhood pushes us to be ever present in our journey with our offspring. It can make us feel so essential and yet so helpless at times. We connect with our strength and yet we notice our vulnerability.

I wholeheartedly believe that we, as mothers, need to value what we bring not only to our children but to the wider world too. It is easy to undervalue what we do, partly because socially motherhood is not given much status but also because it is divided into so many pieces that it is hard to see it as a whole. We cuddle, kiss, soothe, organise, cook, clean, wash, play, plan and so on. Underneath it all though, we are there, giving of ourselves and loving our children.

Exactly how we go about it is up to us. It is essential for us to find our own way of being a mother, releasing ourselves from the prescriptive demands and pressures that are placed on us. I hope this book has started you on the path of considering how you can be the best mother you can be by including yourself in the equation.

I would love at this point to be able to summarize motherhood but that is impossible to do. Instead I want to leave the last word to one of my mothers. As a part of my questionnaire I asked all my women 'What do you wish you knew about motherhood that you know now?' The replies are spread throughout this book depending on the issue that was raised. But the shortest and most simple answer came from Tanya who encountered a pretty bumpy journey to begin with. Despite this she said...

*"You are richer for it."*

This sums up for me what I saw in my women. Despite the challenges, workload and contradictions, as women we become much richer for welcoming children into our lives.

Thank you for reading. If you want to get more information like this you can subscribe to my free monthly newsletter where you will get all the latest articles from The Guilt-Free Guide blog including advanced updates on special offers at:

**www.theguiltfreeguide.co.uk**

# Resources and Further Information

## Blogs

I host a blog called The Guilt-Free Guide to Motherhood where I post articles on a weekly basis on motherhood and also on topics like self-worth. There are regular discussions through the comments about the weekly topic. http://www.theguiltfreeguide.co.uk

## Other Motherhood Blogs

There are lots of blogs out there where mothers speak honestly about the highs and lows of motherhood. There are many types to suit your taste from humorous to straightforward and inspirational. It is really great to hear about the real life exploits of other mothers and build relationships with them. Here are some that I like.

**Thinking Parenting** – Realistic and thought-provoking parenting advice from Anita who acknowledges that there is no perfect way to parent. http://www.anitacleare.co.uk/

**Motherhood: The Real Deal** – This is a straight talking motherhood blog with lots of guest posts and articles on the issues of motherhood. www.motherhoodtherealdeal.com/

**Occupation: (M)other** - A wonderful creative blog following Lucy as she journeys through motherhood https://occupationmother.net/

## Books

There are many great books. I can happily recommend any of these.

*How Not to be a Perfect Mother* by Libby Purves

*Why Love Matters* by Sue Gerhardt

*What Mothers Do Especially When it Looks Like Nothing* by Naomi Stadlen

*Torn in Two* by Rozika Parker

## Support for Crying

Cry-sis is a UK based national charity that has not only information but a support line parents can call when coping with an excessively crying, sleepless or demanding baby. http://www.cry-sis.org.uk

## Birth Trauma

The Birth Trauma Association is a charity that supports women who have had a challenging birth.

http://www.birthtraumaassociation.org.uk/

## Mental Health Support

There are some great information resources out there on the internet which can be a good starting point although they do not tailor their information so can't replace speaking to someone directly.

**Mind** is a UK based charity supporting people with mental health issues. They have information on all mental health issues including Postnatal Depression. http://www.mind.org.uk

**The Royal College of Psychiatrists** have informative leaflets that can be accessed on-line about many mental health issues.

http://www.rcpsych.ac.uk/

**Pandas** is a charity in the UK that supports families who are experiencing pre or postnatal illness in all its forms.

http://www.pandasfoundation.org.uk/

In the United States of America **Postpartum Progress** is a charity to help support women with Postnatal illness. They have a great video on their home page of mothers talking about their experiences and international lists of support resources too.
http://postpartumprogress.org/

**Mental Health America** is a non-profit organisation promoting awareness and support for general mental health issues. They have information on Postnatal illness on their site.
http://www.mentalhealthamerica.net/

**Obsessive Compulsive Disorder**
**OCDUK** is a general site about Obsessive Compulsive Disorder but it also looks into Prenatal and Postnatal OCD  http://www.ocduk.org/

# References

Perel, E. (2007) *Mating in Captivity: Sex, Lies and Domestic Bliss*. Hodder and Stoughton Ltd

Douglas, S J. (2004) *The Mommy Myth: The idealisation of motherhood and how it has undermined all women*. Free Press, Simon & Schuster Inc.